Steve Parish™

PUBLISHING

Amazing Facts about Australian
Native Plants

Text: Cathy Hope

Photography: Steve Parish

Contents

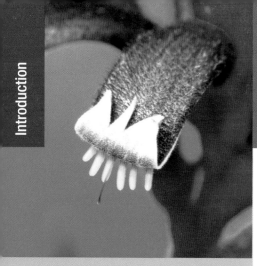

Above: Kangaroo Paw.

Australia's unique
native plants

Australia is a "treasure island". Many of the most amazing plants in the world have evolved in this wonderful land and grow naturally here as native flora. In fact no other country has as many endemic plants. Nowhere else in the world can you find such a range of unusual and brilliantly coloured wildflowers. Australia is a natural garden that excites the senses — inspiring botanists, horticulturalists, photographers, artists and many others.

AUSTRALIA'S ISOLATION has contributed greatly to the evolution of thousands of unique plants. You will discover the importance of biodiversity and experience many amazing facts about Australia's plants as you adventure through the pages of this book.

the FACTS!

OUR LIFE depends on plants. If there were no plants on Earth there would be no people, animals, insects, reptiles, fish or birds.

PLANET EARTH has over 350,000 species of plants. Thousands more will be discovered and named by botanists in the future.

AUSTRALIA HAS more than 24,000 native species of plants, 85% are endemic. That means they originate in Australia and are not native to any other country.

UP TO 100 plant species have become extinct in Australia during the last 220 years.

5031 AUSTRALIAN native plant taxa are listed as rare or threatened.

BOTH WESTERN AUSTRALIA and Queensland each have over 7000 species.

D'ENTRECASTEAUX National Park in South-West Western Australia has recorded 4500 wildflower and tree species.

ULURU–KATA TJUTA National Park has 416 species of flora.

Above: Sturt's Desert Peas.

CATHY HOPE

Above: Golden Grevillea.

AMAZING AMBASSADORS

Australia's plant "treasure" is shared by people from all over the world.

Gold miners from California took more than nuggets home from Australia's 1850s gold rush — they also collected the seeds of local plants that fascinated them.

Australia exports $9 million worth of eucalyptus and acacia seed each year for plantations in 40 countries. Fresh and dried wildflowers also go out around the world as Australian "ambassadors" to a global market worth $40 billion. Many Australian plants have the advantage of being distinctive — with woody stems or robust, showy flowers. The top three "focal fillers" are Kangaroo Paws, Geraldton Wax (right) and Grampians *Thryptomene,* and the best selling feature flowers include banksias, proteas and waratahs. Australian flower exports are worth $400 million, but Australia only supplies 10% of these: other countries, such as Israel, grow large numbers of Australian wildflowers.

Amazing
evolution timeline

Above: Dinosaurs and reptiles dominated the Earth 175 million years ago.

Eon	Era	Period	
Phanerozoic	Cainozoic (Recent Life)	Quaternary Present–1.8 MYA	Today's plant communities result from the events of Earth history.
		Tertiary 65–1.8 MYA	Flowering plants and mammals, dominate this period. The climate is more seasonal, and much drier. Plant species adapt to the new aridity — or become extinct. Today's plants are evolving: *Eucalyptus, Acacia, Banksia* ... Antarctica splits off, isolating Australia.
	Mesozoic (Middle Life)	Cretaceous 141–65 MYA	65 MYA: mass extinctions of flora and fauna (including dinosaurs), possibly due to a huge meteorite. Inland seas retreat. Climate is wet: rainforests are prominent. 125 MYA: First flowering plants.
		Jurassic 205–141 MYA	175 MYA: very wet and hot. Ancestors of Kauri, Wollemi Pine, grass-trees. Many insects. Dinosaurs and reptiles dominate.
		Triassic 250–205 MYA	Cycads and ferns similar to present-day ferns. Gingkoes and conifers (which then dominated the world). True mammals appear. Climate hotter and drier. 245 MYA: Permo-Trias mass extinction
	Palaeozoic (Ancient life)	Permian 298–250 MYA	250 MYA: Mosses and tree ferns are abundant, and seed-bearing conifers. Mammal-like reptiles, crocodiles. 290 MYA: Australia half covered by ice.
		Carboniferous 354–298 MYA	Giant mosses, ferns. Origin of seed plants. Giant amphibians, dragonflies.
		Devonian 410–354 MYA	Ancestors of ferns and mosses.
		Silurian 443–410 MYA	Early vascular land plants: *Cooksonia*.
		Ordovician 490–443 MYA	Plants first creep onto land.
		Cambrian 545–490 MYA	Further evolution of photosynthetic bacteria and algae leads to multi-celled marine plants.
	Proterozoic (Primitive Life)	Late Proterozoic 1000–545 MYA	At this point in time 88% of Earth history has already passed. The Ediacaran Age, named for the South Australian fossil find, is the last stage of the Proterozoic. Multi-cellular animals like jellyfish evolve. 700 MYA: major ice age.
		Mid Proterozoic 1600–1000 MYA	Major ore bodies form in NSW and Qld.
		Early Proterozoic 2500–1600 MYA	The Earth's crust begins to stabilise. The atmosphere stabilises: cyanobacteria are the "architects of the atmosphere".
Archaean		4.5–2500 MYA	The world's oldest known fossils are cyanobacteria. The 3500-million-year-old fossil stromatolites in Western Australia were formed by these organisms, which were vital for the origin of plants. The part of a modern plant cell that makes food from sunlight is its chloroplast and this structure is a cyanobacterium.

*MYA - MILLION YEARS AGO

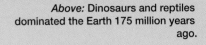

the
FACTS!

EVIDENCE OF EARLIEST LIFE has been found in 3500-million-year-old Australian stromatolite fossils, formed long ago by cyanobacteria.

AUSTRALIA'S WET TROPICS World Heritage-listed rainforests are home to the world's highest concentration of flowering plant families with "primitive" features.

DNA TESTING discovered that eucalypts evolved in Australia about 70 million years ago.

50,000 YEARS AGO the plant eating, flightless ostrich-sized bird, *Genyornis newtoni,* became extinct, possibly due to the firestick burning practices of Aboriginal people.

MUTTABURRASAURUS was named after the town in central Queensland where its fossils were found. The teeth of this 7–8 m dinosaur indicate that it could chew tough vegetation — it may have eaten cycads.

Above: Custard (or Sun) Orchid.

What is
a flowering plant?

the FACTS!

WHITE FLOWERS lack pigment cells. They reflect unwanted sunlight. With petals angled correctly, they can direct the sun's rays to the flower's centre. Trapped heat brings insect pollinators.

EVOLVING TO ATTRACT BIRDS for pollination has meant that many flowers have given up perfume; birds have a poor sense of smell.

BRIGHT RED FLOWERS attract nectar-eating birds, butterflies and mammals with red-sensitive vision. Red flowers look black to insects.

AN INCREDIBLE SHINE EFFECT on some flower petals is due to the petal's starch layer.

INSECTS SEE mainly blue, yellow and ultra-violet. It's estimated that between 65-80% of flowers are pollinated by insects.

There are more than 250,000 flowering plants in the world. The term "Angiosperm" describes the group of flowering plants — it comes from Greek words which indicate that these plants have seeds enclosed in an ovary; the ovule becomes the seed (see generalised flower diagram below). Two sub-groups exist: monocotyledons and dicotyledons.

MONOCOTYLEDONS:

- Examples are lilies, orchids, grasses, grass-trees and palms.
- Flower parts (petals, stamens etc.) are in threes or multiples of three.
- One cotyledon (seed leaf) in the seed.
- Leaves usually have parallel veins.
- Stem with vascular bundles scattered throughout the stem.

DICOTYLEDONS:

- Examples are banksias, eucalypts, *Dampiera*, *Lechenaultia*, peaflowers.
- Flower parts are in fours or fives.
- Two cotyledons (seed leaves) in the seed.
- Leaves with net-like veins.
- Stem with vascular bundles around the inside circle of the stem.

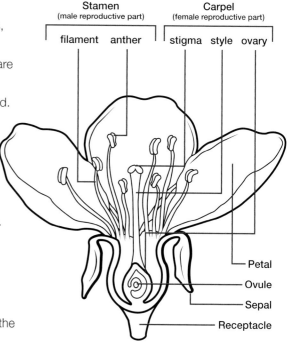

Stamen (male reproductive part) — filament, anther

Carpel (female reproductive part) — stigma, style, ovary

Petal
Ovule
Sepal
Receptacle

LANDING INSTRUCTIONS

Over 50% of flowers have markings, like a runway or spots, to show bees and butterflies where to land: these point the way to nectar. Pale flowers sometimes have invisible honey guides which are only visible under ultraviolet light. Because insects have ultraviolet vision, they can see the pathways on flowers.

Below, top to bottom: Flowers of Eurasian *Potentilla anserina* as seen by humans in natural light; And under ultraviolet (UV) light. Pollinating insects are guided by the strong UV "bull's eye" pattern.

B.JOHN FJORSLETT/INNAMEFOTO

WHAT DO PLANTS NEED?

Sunlight is needed to power the manufacture of food, so the thin, flat shape of leaves maximises their exposure to light, in order to capture it. Photosynthesis is the process by which sugars are produced for food. The part of the cell that makes food is the chloroplast, and this contains the green pigment chlorophyll, which absorbs sunlight. One leaf cell may contain up to 100 chloroplasts, all acting like tiny solar panels. Vital nutrients such as mineral salts are absorbed through roots from the soil and transported by water up the stems to the leaves. Carbon dioxide is taken up from the atmosphere, through breathing holes called stomata in the leaves. Oxygen is "breathed out" as a by-product.

MAGIC SEEDS

Many Australian seeds have evolved to remain dormant until conditions are right for germination. Some wait for rain, and others need a bushfire. Scientists have found a "magic" ingredient — the chemical butenolide in smoke (even when cold) is able to break seed dormancy. It helps activate growth of over 400 native plants.

How are
Australian plants named?

In 1765 Swedish botanist, Carolus Linnaeus, introduced what came to be called the "Linnaean system" — a universal method of classification and naming of each living organism, based on Latin or Greek words that describe it. Such a universal system helps botanists from all over the world understand and communicate with each other even though they may not speak the same language. You will notice that each plant included in this book has several names: a family name, a common or indigenous name and a botanical name.

Above: Pear-fruited Mallee.

BOTANICAL NAME

Each plant is given a two-word botanical name; the first is the "genus" and the second the "species". In this book you will see botanical names in italics. In scientific journals, a botanical name for a plant will include a third name showing the person who named the species.

GENUS (PLURAL GENERA): The first word of the name places the plant in a genus with other plants closely related to it. This generic name always begins with a capital letter.

A group of species in one genus is often given a common name, such as "Kangaroo Paws" for the species in the *Anigozanthus* genus, or "Wattles" for the species in the *Acacia* genus.

SPECIES: The second word of the botanical name gives the plant its own species name. This specific name always begins with a lower-case letter.

COMMON NAME

When an individual plant is given a special common name, capital letters are used for each word, such as Sturt's Desert Pea. A plant may have more than one common name, as people in different areas adopt their own names for plants.

INDIGENOUS NAMES: There are many Aboriginal languages in Australia and the same plant may have different names in different parts of Australia.

FAMILY NAME

A family name is given to a collection of genera having general characteristics. Myrtaceae, the most dominant plant family in Australia, has 1646 species represented by 70 genera, including *Eucalyptus*, *Kunzea*, *Leptospermum*, *Melaleuca* and *Verticordia*. Characteristics that group these genera include having leaves with oil glands and gumnuts.

the FACTS!

BOTANY is the science of plants. People who study plants are scientists called botanists.

TAXONOMISTS are botanists who classify and name plants.

A HERBARIUM houses collections of dried specimens of plants.

DNA SEQUENCING has changed the process of plant classification and naming. It has been revealing unexpected evolutionary relationships.

SCIENTISTS HAVE A VERY complex job trying to decide how different plants are related to each other — or not. Naming of plants reflects what people think about these relationships. As technology gives us more tools, and science advances, so names change. This means that anybody who is interested in plants has a lifelong task keeping abreast of name changes!

Below, left to right: Ashby's Banksia; Round-leafed Tea-tree.

Plant habitats
of Australia

Australia is one of the world's twelve countries classified as "megadiverse". Plants adapt to life in many different areas where soil and climate (amongst other things) have created specific conditions; these places are habitats. Humans can define habitats at many different scales. Seen close-up, a mountain provides windy and calm sides, flat earthy areas and steep rock crevices; but "zoom out" and a range of mountains can be seen as different habitat from a flat sandy desert. Today's "Australia" is a piece of continent that has moved across our planet over hundreds of millions of years, into drier and warmer climates. The millions of square kilometres that were wet forests (millions of years ago) are now savanna grassland and desert — with some remnants of rainforests.

Below, top to bottom: Hummock grassland; Tussock grassland; Heath; Coastal vegetation.

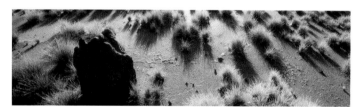

Below, top to bottom: Saltbush; Desert; Salt and temporary lakes; Rainforest; Wet sclerophyll; Dry sclerophyll; Mallee scrublands.

Above, left to right: Heath at D'Entrecasteaux National Park; Shark Bay shore vegetation subject to salt-laden winds; Mulga scrub.

Below, top to bottom: Mulga scrublands; Brigalow scrublands; Woodlands.

Below, top to bottom: Mountain moors; Wetlands; Mixed grassland, savanna and tropical woodlands.

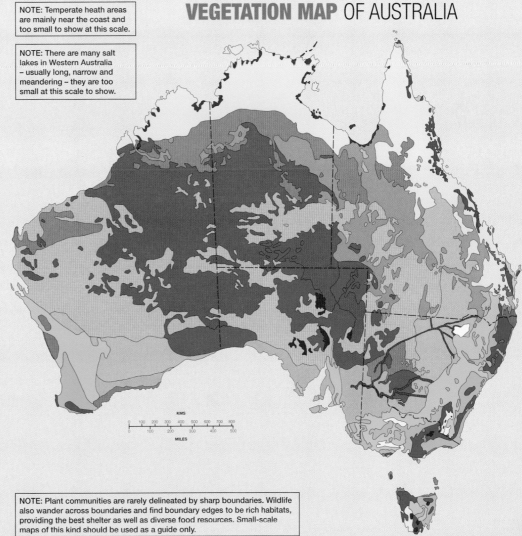

VEGETATION MAP OF AUSTRALIA

1. OCEANS
- Mangrove forests

2. FORESTS
- Tropical rainforest
- Subtropical rainforest
- Warm-temperate rainforest
- Cool-temperate rainforest
- Cloud forest
- Wet sclerophyll forest
- Dry sclerophyll forest

3. TALL AND LOW WOODLANDS
- Monsoon & tropical woodlands
- Temperate & other eucalypt woodlands
- Riverine woodlands
- Semi-arid shrub with savanna
- Arid & semi-arid low woodlands

4. SHRUBLANDS AND SCRUBLANDS
- Mallee
- Acacia – Mulga
- Acacia – Brigalow
- Saltbush/Bluebush

5. HEATHS
- Wallum
- Temperate

6. GRASSLANDS AND SEDGELANDS
- Northern grasslands
- Desert grasslands
- Temperate grasslands
- Cool-temperate grasslands
- Cold-climate grasslands & sedgelands

7. EXTREME HABITATS
- Alpine herbfields
- Salt lakes

NOTE: Temperate heath areas are mainly near the coast and too small to show at this scale.

NOTE: There are many salt lakes in Western Australia – usually long, narrow and meandering – they are too small at this scale to show.

NOTE: Plant communities are rarely delineated by sharp boundaries. Wildlife also wander across boundaries and find boundary edges to be rich habitats, providing the best shelter as well as diverse food resources. Small-scale maps of this kind should be used as a guide only.

Banksias
— sweet, showy & tough

Above: A New Holland Honeyeater on a banksia flower.

Family: Proteaceae
Genus: Banksia

Australia has 77 species of Banksia. They are named after Sir Joseph Banks (1743–1820) who voyaged with Captain James Cook on the ship Endeavour. As they explored the east coast of Australia in 1770, they collected specimens of Australian plants. Banks collected Saw Leaf Banksia (Banksia serrata) which grows in coastal areas of Queensland, New South Wales, Victoria and Tasmania, and it became the first Banksia to be officially named.

the FACTS!

HONEYEATER TONGUE and banksia flower shapes match, to show a long relationship. Scientists think they evolved closely together.

HONEY-FLAVOURED NECTAR is abundant in banksia flowers, providing a great feast for birds and small marsupials. In return, these visitors are dusted with pollen which they transfer to other flowers.

NECTAR-FEEDING BIRDS such as Lorikeets and Silvereyes follow the flowering seasons of different *Banksia* species, constantly seeking the next place to feed.

MOONLIGHT DINING by possums and bats is greatly assisted by banksias with light and bright blooms that show up at night.

TINY HONEY POSSUMS are nectarivores. Their brush-tipped tongues probe into banksia flowers to gather nectar.

AUSTRALIAN AUTHOR May Gibbs wrote of a grotesque and scary character in her famous children's book *Snugglepot and Cuddlepie*. She turned a hairy hobgoblin "cone" from *Banksia serrata* into the character, "Big Bad Banksia Man".

GREG HARM/SPP

WHAT A USEFUL PLANT

Aboriginal people from Groote Eylandt and the Top End had several uses for Swamp Banksia (*B. dentata*). Flowers gave them nectar to eat and to mix with water for a sweet drink. Dry old cones were smeared with animal fat and set alight to use as torches or to transfer fire. Old cones were even used as hairbrushes.

In the Grampians, banksia flowers were used to filter muddy water

Early settlers in south-eastern areas made bullock yokes from the timber of Coastal Banksia (*B. integrifolia*).

Far left: A Honey Possum sips banksia nectar with its brush-tipped tongue.

Left: Coastal Banksia (*Banksia integrifolia*) is the floral emblem of the City of Frankston, Victoria.

Conservation Watch

Land clearing, picking from the wild for the cut flower industry, climate change and the dreaded disease Cinnamon Fungus (*Phytophthora cinnamomi*) are all threats to banksias.

Above: Commercial picking of much admired Scarlet Banksia (*Banksia coccinea*) is now banned from crown land.

TASMANIA'S EXTINCT BANKSIA

Charles Denison King AM (1909-1991), was passionately interested in the flora of Tasmania during his lifetime. Deep in one of Tasmania's mines he found a 38,000-year-old banksia "cone" which had been preserved in a sedimentary layer.

This banksia relic was discovered to be from an extinct species which was named *Banksia kingii* to honour "Deny" King.

Above: Scarlet Banksia (*Banksia coccinea*).

BANKSIA "CONES" — FIREPROOF CAPSULES

Most banksia "cones" are incredibly tough — to stop animals and birds from eating their seeds. Many hold their seeds firmly enclosed until a bushfire rages through the stand of shrubs or trees. Chemicals in smoke promote germination of the seeds. After the heat has forced the "lips" of the follicles to open up like little "mouths" (right) so the seeds can fall out, with superb timing, onto an ash bed. The perfect place to grow.

Right: Detail of open follicles on a banksia "cone".

Below, left to right: Cutleaf Banksia (*Banksia praemorsa*) is native to Western Australia. The flowers' odour is said to smell like rotten meat pies; Acorn Banksia (*Banksia prionotes*).

the FACTS!

POSSUM BANKSIA (*B. baueri*) has big fluffy grey-mauve flowers — they look quite like a curled-up possum.

TENNIS BALL BANKSIA (*B. laevigata*) has tennis ball-shaped flowers.

HAIRPIN BANKSIA (*B. spinulosa,* below) flowers look as though hundreds of fine hairpins have been inserted into them.

ACORN BANKSIA (*B. prionotes,* left) has flowers shaped like acorns from an oak tree.

"BIRTHDAY CANDLES" is a *Banksia* cultivar available from plant nurseries.

11

Bell Flowers
— shaped for birds

Above: Yellow-faced Honeyeater feeding at *Blandfordia* species flower.

Family: Blandfordiaceae
Genus: Blandfordia

CHRISTMAS BELLS

Four species of Christmas Bells bring cheer to Australia's festive season, with their bright red and yellow waxy bell-shaped flowers. They also bring seasonal gifts to nectar-feeding birds such as honeyeaters.

Christmas Bell (*Blandfordia grandiflora*) once thrived in coastal swamplands of South-East Queensland and New South Wales. It is now rare due to draining of swampland for housing, pine plantations and wild harvesting. Year after year, people picked the flowers in the lead-up to Christmas and set up roadside stalls to sell them.

the FACTS!

WINTER-FLOWERING *CORREA* species number eleven, are endemic to Australia, and found mainly in south-east coastal heathlands.

DENBLY GARDENS at Killarney in Victoria has a special collection of *Correa* species, featuring about 120 varieties and cultivars.

***CORREA* SEED COATS** protect the seed and prevent most germination — until after a bushfire.

NARROW, BELL-SHAPED flowers produce plenty of nectar, which attracts bees, honeyeaters and other nectar-loving birds. Honeyeaters are crafty birds and have been known to take shortcuts. They will use their beak to pierce a hole in the side of the bell, making it easier to reach the nectar.

Right, top: Tasmanian Christmas Bell (*Blandfordia punicea*) is an endemic species growing on hillsides and damp heaths, from coastal to subalpine areas of Tasmania.

Right: Native Fuchsia (*Correa reflexa*). Australia's best known *Correa* species grows in all States of Australia except the Northern Territory. It is not a real *Fuchsia* species, but takes its common name from their similar looks.

BORONIA

Family: Rutaceae
Genus: Boronia

There are about 104 Boronia species in the world; most are endemic to Australia. New Caledonia has four species.

FLOWERS HAVE FOUR PETALS and eight stamens making cup or star-shaped bells.

Australia's Brown Boronia (*Boronia megastigma*) has such an amazing fragrance that it has become world famous and is considered to be Australia's most fragrant plant. Interestingly there are some people who cannot smell this unforgettable fragrance. The cup-shaped flowers are a unique combination of chocolate brown on the outside and yellow inside. Commercial crops are grown in Australia, New Zealand, California, Israel, South Africa and Europe, either for the cut flower trade or for extraction of oil for the perfume industry.

Above, top to bottom: Mauve Boronia (*Boronia denticulata*); Brown Boronia (*Boronia megastigma*).

Conservation Watch

Yellow Mountain Bell (*Darwinia collina*, below) is Endangered and grows on the slopes of Bluff Knoll in the Stirling Range in Western Australia.

Above: Cranbrook Bell belongs to the family Myrtaceae. Within the apparent red "petals" (actually bracts) nestle more typical myrtaceous flowers.

DARWINIA — MOUNTAIN BELLS

Over 60 species of *Darwinia*, known as Mountain Bells, are endemic to Australia — with about 50 species in Western Australia. Cranbrook Bell (*Darwinia meeboldii*), vivid in red, white and green, flowers from September to November in one area of dense heath on stony slopes at the western end of Western Australia's Stirling Range.

Above: Yellow Mountain Bell (*Darwinia collina*).

FLORAL EMBLEM

Royal Bluebell (*Wahlenbergia gloriosa*) presents vivid bluebell flowers during spring in woodland habitats at altitudes above 1300 m. Royal Bluebell's distribution is limited to ACT, south-eastern NSW and eastern Victoria. It is the floral emblem for the Australian Capital Territory.

Left: ACT's floral emblem, the Royal Bluebell.

the FACTS!

THE WORLD HAS about 200 species of Bluebells belonging to the *Wahlenbergia* genus. They are found in countries such as Australia, New Zealand and South America.

AUSTRALIA HAS 26 species of Bluebells — annual or perennial herbs enjoying many habitats from the red desert sands of central Australia, to alpine locations.

CROWEA

The world's only three species of *Crowea*, often called wax flowers, are all endemic to Australia. Bell-shaped *Crowea* buds open into a star-shaped flower with five petals. *Croweas* germinate more readily after being "smoke stimulated" by a bushfire. These frost-tolerant, drought-resistant, attractive plants, are highly valued for cultivation. New South Wales' Pink Wax (*Crowea saligna*), grows near Sydney in Hawkesbury sandstone.

Above: Several small marsupials including Sugar Gliders, feed on nectar from callistemons.

Callistemon
— sweet on the tooth

Family: Myrtaceae
Genus: Callistemon

Australia has 34 species of Callistemon. *The most outstanding feature of these flowers is their stunning "stand–out" stamens in red, pink, cream, green or mauve. Every Bottlebrush spike is made up of many individual flowers, all with prominent stamens. The anthers on some* Callistemon *species, such as Gold-tipped Bottlebrush (*Callistemon polandii*), absolutely glow, adding charm and contrast to flower spikes.*

the FACTS!

CALLISTEMON SEED was first taken to England in 1789 by patron of botany Sir Joseph Banks.

WHILE ON THE "VOYAGE to Terra Australis" with Matthew Flinders, during 1814, botanist Robert Brown named the genus *Callistemon*.

HOLD A CALLISTEMON LEAF against the light and you can see hundreds of minute oil glands.

OIL EXTRACTS from the leaves of some callistemons are being examined by scientists and tested for use as natural herbicides.

AUSTRALIAN CALLISTEMONS are cultivated in Kathmandu Valley, in Nepal's Himalayan Mountains.

TINY WOODY NUTS containing seed often remain on the stems of callistemons for years. Fire stimulates the nuts to open, releasing the seed. Germination happens about three weeks after seeds experience the right conditions for growth.

Below: A callistemon flower stalk makes a perfect perch for a nectar-feeding New Holland Honeyeater.

MOST *CALLISTEMON* SPECIES occur in the east and south-east of Australia with only two species in the south-west of Western Australia. They are often found thriving in damp soil beside a stream or near another water source.

Mt Annan Botanic Garden in New South Wales has a feature garden displaying more than 30 *Callistemon* species (and many cultivars).

Left to right: Bottlebrushes in east-coast eucalypt forest; Gold-tipped Bottlebrush (*Callistemon polandii*).

LOW WATER DEMAND

Willow Bottlebrush (*Callistemon salignus*, below) is native to Qld, NSW, Vic and SA. It also has another common name — Paperbark Bottlebrush — because of its white, papery bark. This plant is grown at Lower Richmond, on the north coast of New South Wales, to help improve the health of the wetlands.

Beaufortia
— beautiful

Family: Myrtaceae
Genus: Beaufortia

Beaufortia *species, some of the brightest and most stunning Bottlebrushes, are difficult to grow away from their natural habitat in Western Australia, so are not common in cultivation. They are especially difficult to grow in eastern Australia.*

FLOWERS ARE ARRANGED in a small bottlebrush or tufted shape in vibrant reds, purples, oranges, golds and sometimes cream. The small, almost heath-like, leaves are generally crowded in alternating pairs set at right angles to each other. Sand Bottlebrush (*Beaufortia squarrosa*), is a drought-tolerant species of coastal plains in Western Australia. In the south, near Busselton, plants have brilliant, flame-red flowers and in northern locations, as far as the Murchison River above Geraldton, flowers are orange and yellow.

Left: Gravel Bottlebrush (*Beaufortia decussata*) grows in Jarrah forests near Albany and in the scrub of the Stirling Range in eastern Australia.

the FACTS!

LITTLE BOTTLEBRUSH
(*Beaufortia micrantha*, below) is the smallest species of *Beaufortia*, growing to just over half a metre tall. It's found on heaths from Lake Grace south-east to Esperance in Western Australia.

Above: Sand Bottlebrush (*Beaufortia squarrosa*).

BEAUFORTIA SPECIES ARE NAMED in honour of Mary, Duchess of Beaufort (1630–1714), a royal patron of botany.

Below: Stirling Range Bottlebrush (*Beaufortia heterophylla*).

ON THE MENU

The tiny Honey Possum (*Tarsipes rostratus*), confined to the south-west of Australia, is dependent on nectar and pollen-producing blooms for its food supply. Fortunately for this small marsupial, nature has organised for different plants to be in flower each month of the year. During spring and summer, flowering *Beaufortia* species are on the menu for Honey Possums as they scamper over blooms, probing their long brush-tipped tongues into the flowers to soak up the nectar.

M. & I. MORCOMBE

Carnivorous Plants
— pitfall traps

Family: Cephalotaceae & Nepenthaceae
Genus: Cephalotus (1 species), Nepenthes (3 species)

Australia has four species of pitcher plant. "Pitcher" is another name for a jug. Some plants' pitchers are as big as a jug and others' are as small as a cap on a marking pen. Passive trapping by a pitcher is just one of five ways that carnivorous plants have found to catch food.

Above: Albany Pitcher Plant
(*Cephalotus follicularis*).

PRISONERS IN PITCHERS

These weird plants thrill people with their seemingly un-plantlike taste for luring, trapping and consuming juicy insects — and occasionally even small animals.

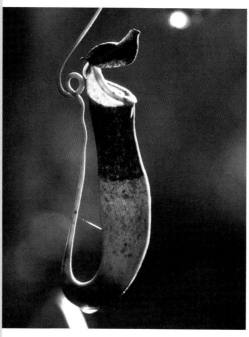

Above: Close up of rim of pitcher and insect.

Below, top to bottom: Pitcher plant *Nepenthes mirabilis* grows beside streams in tropical areas of Queensland such as Cape York Peninsula. Plants often climb around other vegetation for support and produce quite large pitchers, which grow to about 20 cm.

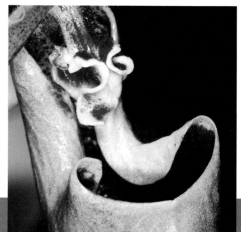

the FACTS!

FOUR PITCHER PLANT species are native to Australia, and they belong to two different families.

SOME PEOPLE grow carnivorous plants as an environmentally friendly way to reduce insects in the house. Pitcher plants are excellent fly and ant-catchers and Sundews can capture pesky mosquitoes.

THE PITCHER MIMICS a flower, and so tricks insects into landing and falling in. Actually the pitcher structure is a modified leaf.

A PITCHER'S LID is normally open, but can be shut during hot weather to stop evaporation and to keep out excessive rain.

SOME TINY TREE-FROGS are remarkable in that they make a home inside a pitcher plant. They somehow avoid being digested by the plant, and live by snatching insects that fall into the pitcher.

Australian pitcher plants live in wet, grassy areas, savannas and swamps — often at forest or creek margins. Swampy soils are poor in nutrients, so the plants need another source of energy. The solution to their problem is to gain nitrogen and protein by luring, trapping, drowning and digesting animals that provide a healthy feast. Scent that humans can't smell attracts unwary visitors to the rim of the pitcher. They are tempted inside to sweet nectar — and a slippery, waxy surface. All of a sudden they lose their grip and slide down into a watery grave. The struggling creature stimulates the pitcher to produce digestive juices to dissolve the corpse. Alternatively bacteria break down the body.

— nature's flypapers

Family: Droseraceae, Lentibulariaceae
Genus: Drosera, Utricularia

The sundews' approach to carnivory is to use sticky mucilage to trap insects. The glistening drops of mucilage give them their common name. Australia has about 70 of the world's approximately 100 species, and Australia and New Zealand share some species. Almost three-quarters of world sundew species are found in Western Australia, and central Australia's desert has two species found near waterholes.

Above: Pink Rainbow Sundew (*Drosera menziesii*).

SINISTER SUNDEWS

In Australia, sundews grow in mossy, damp conditions in a range of habitats from alpine to tropical. These bizarre plants lure insects to their death. When an insect lands on a leaf, it is captured and imprisoned by the sticky "tentacle-like" hairs that bend over and squash the insect against the leaf. Insects are dissolved into a liquid that the plant can absorb.

Alpine Sundew (*Drosera arcturi*) flowers in midsummer in damp, mossy alpine areas of Tas, Vic and NSW in Australia and also in New Zealand. In Tasmania it is often found growing amongst Cushion Plants.

the FACTS!

AUSTRALIA HAS about 60 of the world's 214 species of Bladderworts — in the genus *Utricularia* belonging to the Lentibulariaceae family.

FLOWERS have an "apron-like" lip and appear in colours including white, yellow, pink, blue and purple.

THE BUBBLE-LIKE BLADDERS of Bladderworts have "trapdoors". This way of trapping food is praised as the cleverest of any plant. When a tiny creature hits a guide hair, the hair's movement breaks the trapdoor seal. There is no escape; the trapdoor springs open, water rushes into the bladder carrying the creature, and the door shuts, locking the prisoner in. Chemicals in the bladder dissolve the body, so the plant can absorb its nutrients.

Below: A unique point about Red Ink Sundew (*Drosera erythrorhiza*) is that the flowers grow in the earth before being exposed to the light. The plant has a bright red underground tuber. Large groups of Red Ink Sundews grow in sandy areas between Three Springs and Ongerup in Western Australia.

Above: Purple Daisy Bush (*Olearia rudis*), a true shrub rather than an annual, or a perennial herb.

Daisies
— life in a large family

Family: Asteraceae

SENECIO DAISIES

The *Senecio* genus is large, with about 2000 species worldwide. Australia has about 50 species, and most are bright yellow. Annual Yellow Top (*Senecio gregorii*), an annual, is often seen flourishing in South Australia and central Australia. Butterflies, like the female Caper White Butterfly (below), love these daisies. They use the petals as a landing platform from which to probe for nectar.

PETER SLATER

OLEARIA DAISIES

Australia has 130 endemic species of the world's 190 *Olearia* daisies. These vary from annual herbs to shrubs and small trees. The daisy colour range includes white, cream, yellow, pink, blue and purple. Purple Daisy Bush (*Olearia rudis*) is a one-metre-high shrub, growing in NSW, Vic, SA and WA. It is found on some of Western Australia's goldfields.

Above: Swan River Daisy (*Brachyscome iberidifolia*) grows naturally in limestone and sandy soils in NT, WA and SA. The flowers on this tiny annual can be white, purple, mauve or blue. This is a daisy that has been cultivated for many years.

Left: New South Wales' Pilliga Daisy (*Brachyscome formosa*), a low-growing pinkish-mauve daisy, has found its way to England where it is now grown in rockeries and in hanging baskets. It's a frost-resistant plant that spreads by suckering.

the FACTS!

THE ASTERACEAE FAMILY has over 20,000 species worldwide.

A DAISY LOOKS LIKE a single flower, but the centre is actually a composite bloom, made up of hundreds of tiny individual flowers surrounded by bracts.

AUSTRALIAN GRASSLANDS are important habitats for native daisies.

A FEATHERY "PARACHUTE" adorns the seeds of many daisy species to assist in wind dispersal.

AUSTRALIA'S EPHEMERAL (short-lived, annual) everlasting daisies have evolved over millions of years to survive life in the arid zone by being "avoiders". They remain dormant during times of high stress such as intense heat or cold and lack of water.

BUTTERFLIES such as Painted Ladies and Monarchs can be attracted to your garden by growing a variety of everlasting daisies.

THE SWEET FRAGRANT, sometimes sickly, perfume of many everlasting daisies entices ants to visit the flowers. In doing so, ants assist in the pollination process.

SEEDS OF THESE plants have inbuilt survival kits with a chemical growth inhibitor.

Everlasting Daisies
— carpets of colour

Above: White Everlasting Daisy.

Family: Asteraceae

Australia has hundreds of species of "everlasting" daisies with papery bracts, belonging to such genera as: Anemocarpa, Chrysocephalum, Lawrencella, Rhodanthe, Schoenia, Waitzia *and* Xerochrysum.

LIKE THE DESERT AFTER RAIN

Australia's arid interior has a high number of low-rainfall years, interspersed with few years of high rainfall. During years of low rainfall, small colonies of everlastings may struggle, but after heavy, soaking rain a miraculous transformation of the desert takes place. Breathtaking multi-hued carpets of annuals — predominantly everlasting daisies — create an unforgettable aura across the terracotta tones of the land.

PINK PAPER DAISY

Western Australia's Pink Paper Daisy (*Rhodanthe chlorocephala* ssp. *rosea,* above), germinates in response to rain, flowering about ten weeks later in prettiest pinks.

This internationally famous everlasting daisy has been enjoyed globally for hundreds of years. Scandinavian gardeners have noted that it grows rapidly with so much light during the lengthy days of the far northern summer.

EVERLASTING PAPER TRAIL

The star-shaped, delicate crepe-paper-like daisies of Chamomile Sunray (*Rhodanthe anthemoides,* far right) are so prolific during summer that they create a "blizzard of white" in moist, alpine meadows and grasslands in Vic, ACT, NSW, Qld and Tas. Their aroma is suggestive of a chamomile fragrance and attracts butterflies. This everlasting is very popular in cultivation.

COMMON EVERLASTING

Common Everlasting (*Chrysocephalum apiculatum*), a perennial, is found over much of Australia in varied habitats including rugged coastlines, fertile grasslands, forests, alpine meadows and arid deserts. It is frequently cultivated in Australia and is a highly suitable town landscaping plant. Its prostrate nature makes it excellent for roundabouts and highway garden strips, as it does not impede the vision of motorists.

Conservation Watch

One of South Africa's daisies, Purple Ragwort (*Senecio elegans*), with cerise-pink flowers, has spread to, and is growing on the coastlines of New Zealand and Australia. Some of the *Senecio* species spread very rapidly and can become weeds.

RIGHT: CATHY HOPE

Above: Chamomile Sunray (*Rhodanthe anthemoides*).

GOLDEN EVERLASTING DAISY

Golden Everlasting (*Xerochrysum bracteatum*), is an extremely variable annual or perennial plant, found over most of Australia in all habitats. Some have very long flowering periods. It is the only everlasting daisy growing in tropical Darwin and the Gulf of Carpentaria.

Above: Common Dampiera (*Dampiera linearis*) is a spreading, low-growing plant cultivated and sold as "Violet Princess". In spring and summer, metre-wide patches of this blue flower brighten bushland from Geraldton to the south coast of Western Australia.

Dampiera
— botanical blues

Family: Goodeniaceae
Genus: Dampiera

Flowers of every hue of blue, from the palest blues, sky blue, royal blue through to deep blues and purple, are dominant in the Dampiera genus. A few pink, white and yellow flowering species exist as well. These herbaceous perennial plants vary from being prostrate and spreading to growing as a small shrub. Each flower has five heart-shaped petals.

GROWN OVERSEAS

Dampiera diversifolia (right), a native of South West Australia, is much admired by visitors who see it growing at the National Botanic Garden of Wales', "Australian Garden" in Britain. This sought-after, prostrate perennial is widely cultivated in gardens throughout Australia.

the FACTS!

THE GENUS *DAMPIERA* is endemic to Australia, with 66 named species. Western Australia has almost two thirds of the species. Central Australia and the Northern Territory have three species.

WILLIAM DAMPIER (1652–1715) was the first person to collect and report on the blue flowers of New Holland (Australia's name in those days). The genus is named for him.

WE SEE COLOUR IN FLOWERS as a result of light being reflected from plant pigments to our eyes. But these colours don't exist *for* humans — they have evolved to suit the vision of various pollinators. *Dampiera* species is pollinated by insects.

PURPLE FLOWERING, Kangaroo Island Dampiera (*Dampiera lanceolata* var. *insularis*) is endemic to Kangaroo Island in South Australia.

BLUE DAMPIERA (*Dampiera stricta*) is the only species growing naturally in Tasmania. This same species is also found in coastal areas of Qld, NSW and Vic.

MANY *DAMPIERA* SPECIES spread by suckering.

PIRATE PICKS WILDFLOWERS

Long ago in 1688, the crew from an English pirate ship *Cygnet* came ashore near King Sound in north-west Australia. One of the pirates, William Dampier, became very famous due to his skilled navigation, map-making, exploration and great interest in Australia's natural features. He returned to England with pressed wildflower specimens. During 1699 he sailed again to Western Australia, as captain of the ship HMS *Roebuck*, and picked more wildflowers. Twenty-four of Dampier's specimens, including Blue Dampiera, are held in Britain's Oxford Herbarium. Dampier is often said to be Australia's first European natural historian.

Left: Common Dampiera (*Dampiera linearis*).

Below: Pouched Dampiera (*Dampiera sacculata*) flowers in great profusion from September to October. Its habitat is heathlands and swampy areas of Western Australia, in such places as Esperance, the Stirling Ranges and between Bunbury and Augusta.

Dryandra
— honeypot plants

Conservation Watch

It's estimated that 28% of *Dryandra* species will disappear with an increase of 0.5 °C global warming, above the present annual average. Six *Dryandra* species are already classified as Endangered with a high risk of Extinction in the future.

Family: Proteaceae
Genus: Dryandra

Australia has 93 species of Dryandra, *all endemic to the south-west of Australia. King Dryandra (*Dryandra proteoides*), with the largest flower of all dryandra species, could easily be mistaken for a South African Protea. Three species are commercially grown for their sensational, long-lasting blooms. Dryandras prefer limestone-based sandy heaths and woodlands and have a mass of very fine roots, giving plants a better chance to take up nutrients. Foliage, often tough and serrated, is very similar to that of banksias. Some, like Showy Dryandra (*Dryandra formosa*), even have leaves arranged around the flower like legs on a octopus.*

DNA DISCOVERY

There has always been adventure, challenge, frustration and reward for botanists in trying to identify plants. When plants have many similarities the challenge increases, and dryandras and banksias have tested many botanists over the years. DNA is making a difference. The journal, *Australian Systematic Botany* published a paper in late 2007 by Austin Mast and Kevin Thiele. These researchers presented evidence that dryandras are actually banksias, and so all these species have undergone name changes. In future, enthusiasts who keep up-to-date with naming will not mention *Dryandra* species — but many others will.

Above: Prickly Dryandra (*Dryandra salcata*).

MOST DRYANDRA flowers produce honey-scented sweet nectar, over a long period, which is much appreciated by birds, insects and beekeepers. In fact, several of these plants have been given common names such as Summer Honeypot and Yellow Honeypot.

Above: Parrot Bush (*Dryandra sessilis*) flowering in the winter and spring produces great honey. Aboriginal people of the Nyungar area call this plant Pudjak.

Left: Showy Dryandra (*Dryandra formosa*).

the FACTS!

SOME DRYANDRAS, especially the low-growing prostrate species, are really weird as they have underground stems with flowers at ground level. Why would this be? Perhaps they evolved to prevent predators from destroying the plant, or maybe it was protection against a harsh climate.

***DRYANDRA* SPECIES** have been growing in Australia for millions of years. Fossilised *Dryandra* species plants have been discovered in brown coal deposits in Victoria.

DURING the late Palaeocene period, about 56 million years ago, *Dryandra* species were also growing in New South Wales. Fossilised leaves have been found in sediment, identical to the narrow saw-toothed leaves of *Dryandra formosa*.

Emu Bushes
— lovers of desert

Family: Myoporaceae
Genus: Eremophila

Emu Bushes belong to Eremophila, *one of the largest genera in Australia with 215 species — most in Western Australia. Tasmania has no species and New Zealand has a single species,* Eremophila debilis. *Emus and bush turkeys eat the fleshy fruit. Their fuchsia-like flowers come in a great colour range including white, pink, blue, green, mauve, purple, red, orange and yellow. Most species are drought, frost and fire resistant.*

Right: Golden Spotted Emu Bush (*E. maculata* var. *aurea*).

the FACTS!

SPOTTED EMU BUSH (*Eremophila maculata*, above), growing near the Kimberley region, is known to contain hydrocyanic acid in the foliage and is poisonous to stock.

75% OF *EREMOPHILA* SPECIES have flowers that have evolved to attract insects for pollination. Spotty markings lead bees, butterflies and other insects into the throat of the flower to be dusted with pollen.

25% OF *EREMOPHILA* SPECIES flowers suit the requirements of nectar-feeding birds such as honeyeaters — and so use them as pollinators.

MEAT HOUSE ROOFS constructed by early settlers were thatched with Turpentine Bush (*Eremophila sturtii*). Flies hate the sticky leaves which smell of turpentine.

THE NAME *EREMOPHILA* comes from the Greek words "eremos" (desert) and "phileo" (love). So this is a genus of "desert-lovers". Emu Bushes survive during severe drought by dropping leaves, by not flowering and/or not setting fruit.

FROM THE CRADLE TO THE GRAVE

Berrigan (*Eremophila longifolia*) has a sacred status for many Indigenous people in Central Australia. This plant is used during many rituals and ceremonies to decorate pierced nostrils, armbands and headbands. When a baby is born, branches of foliage are thrown in the fire to produce fumes to "smoke" the baby and mother. This practice is said to make the baby strong and help the mother stop bleeding after the birth and to give her a good milk supply for the baby. When someone dies, branches are used to cover the body and line the grave. *Eremophila longifolia* also grows in NSW, Qld, Vic, SA and WA.

Above: Latrobe's Emu Bush (*Eremophila latrobei*).

Left: Berrigan (*E. longifolia*). This genus tends to have hairy stems and leaves and a blue-grey colour for improved heat deflection.

Feather Flowers
— heart turners

Conservation Watch

In the past these Feather Flowers have been over-picked from their bushland setting to be sold as cut flowers. To overcome this problem, growers are now cultivating more than twenty species for the floristry trade.

Family: Myrtaceae
Genus: Verticordia

Verticordia species splash patches of their fluffy massed flowers across Western Australia's sand plains and heathlands. Colours include the brightest yellows, orange, pink and red. These beautiful flowers with five petals are called Feather Flowers, because each flower has a dramatically fringed calyx, giving a very appealing feathery look. It is said that there are species in flower during every month of the year. Spring-flowering Verticordia chrysostachys, of the sandheaths between Geraldton and Kalbarri, produces spikes of golden yellow flowers, which become blotched with red as they age.

Above: Yellow Feather Flower (*Verticordia chrysantha*).

Above: Verticordia verticillata is very tall for a Feather Flower, growing as a small white flowering tree to a height of five metres. The position of these trees, in sandy areas of the Kimberleys, indicates nearby elevated groundwater.

Above: Splendid Feather Flower (*Verticordia brachypoda*).

the FACTS!

VERTICORDIA is an Australian genus with over 100 described species. One is native to South Australia and the others are found in Western Australia. One of the Western Australian species extends into the Northern Territory and also north Queensland.

MERREDIN in Western Australia has proudly chosen the bright yellow *Verticordia chrysantha* as the town's floral emblem.

ONE OF THE *VERTICORDIA* SPECIES looks like a cauliflower when it has a dome of white flowers from Nov-Dec in locations from Mingenew to Lake King. Wild Cauliflower (*Verticordia eriocephala*) also grows at Kings Park in Perth.

KINGS PARK IN PERTH has a display of many *Verticordia* species growing in the Federation Walkway.

FLORAL TRADE OF FEATHER FLOWERS

Learning to cultivate *Verticordia* species has been a battle for horticulturalists. There is only one seed in each flower, and germination rates are fairly poor. A secret to successfully grow plants has been to graft *Verticordia* cuttings onto a close relative, *Darwinia citriodora*. Widely cultivated Plume Feather Flower (*Verticordia plumosa*) which occurs naturally on granite slopes from Perth to the south coast, was the first species of *Verticordia* to be described by the botanist de Candolle.

Ferns
— forest air conditioners

Above: Crow's Nest Fern (*Asplenium australasicum*), abundant in rainforests throughout Australia and the South Pacific, is most often found growing high up on other vines or trees. These light-seeking, epiphytic plants are not parasites — as they collect their own food and water for survival. Ferns like these provide habitats for invertebrates and great basking places for large pythons.

the FACTS!

"THE PTERIDOPHYTES" is the group to which all the ferns belong. Australia has over 400 of the world's approximately 10,000 fern species.

LOOK UNDERNEATH a fern frond. The little spots you see are spore cases, which will break open when mature, releasing fine spores to be windblown to other locations.

SPORE PRODUCTION is a very primitive method of plant reproduction. Ferns do not develop flowers to produce seeds.

A TINY SPORE develops a small flat, heart-shaped plant called a prothallus from which the new fern develops.

A "FIDDLEHEAD" is the name given to the tightly curled frond of new fern growth — because it looks like the handle of a violin or fiddle.

AUSTRALIA'S KING FERN (*Angiopteris evecta*), is said to have the largest fronds in the world, at seven metres. King Fern is rare, growing only at Carnarvon Gorge, Fraser Island and few Qld localities.

Division: Pteridophyta

Australia's richest fern habitat, which showcases about 65% of Australia's fern species, occurs in the wet tropical rainforests of Queensland, such as the Daintree. This fern flora amounts to about 240 species with at least 46 endemic to the Queensland rainforests. Ferns don't feature to the same extent in Western Australia, where there are about 50 species. Ferns contribute greatly to the health of rainforests by helping to maintain humidity, by adding organic matter to the soil and by providing shelter for living creatures.

ANCIENT FOSSIL FERNS

True ferns evolved about 325 million years ago, during the Carboniferous Period, but even older fossils have been found, including one from Einasleigh in Queensland, dated at 340 million years old. Fossils from the later Permian Period include the 255-million-year-old trunk of a tree fern found at Blackwater in Queensland, and a 220-million-year-old Fork-frond Seed Fern, *Dicroidium zuberi*, from Dubbo in New South Wales.

Above: Petrified tree fern trunk.

Left: Coral fern (*Gleichenia microphylla*) is found along waterways and in swamps in New Zealand, Malaysia and in every State of Australia except the Northern Territory. Stockmen, campers and mountain hikers in Tasmanian alpine areas have been known to gather the fronds to make temporary dry beds, often directly on top of the snow.

TREE FERNS

Tree ferns are only endemic to countries in the Southern Hemisphere. Tree ferns of the *Dicksonia* genus were widespread on the southern supercontinent Gondwana about 200 million years ago, and Australia now has three of the world's 25 *Dicksonia* species. Soft Tree Fern (*Dicksonia antarctica*) grows to a height of 15 metres in moist mountain gullies and misty damp rainforests.

FERNS FOR FOOD

Aborigines were very careful not to kill tree ferns, and instead of harvesting the fronds, they opened up the top half of the stem to remove the starchy pith. This contains 12% carbohydrate and can be eaten raw or cooked. Aboriginal people in Australia and Maoris in New Zealand knew not to eat the poisonous green fronds of Bracken, but dug up the rhizomes, which contain mucilaginous starch, to prepare as a staple food.

Top: Tree ferns around Russell Falls in Mt Field National Park, Tasmania.

Right: Orange-eyed Tree-frogs live amongst tree ferns in the canopy of moist, warm rainforests. These frogs gather in large numbers on the fronds of tree ferns where the males compete against each other, croaking their mating calls during a breeding frenzy.

Below: Bracken Fern (*Pteridium esculentum*).

the FACTS!

THOUGH BRACKEN FERN (*Pteridium esculentum*) is a native of Australia and New Zealand, it acts as a noxious weed due to alteration of its habitat. It grows aggressively on cleared land.

THE POISON PTAQUILOSIDE is found in Bracken fronds, as an evolutionary defence against insects. The poison is a type of cyanide. Cattle eating bracken risk developing cancer tumours in their bladder and haemorrhages throughout their body due to bone marrow damage. Horses eating bracken may develop nervous symptoms as the poison causes a thiamine deficiency.

JUICE FROM BRACKEN STEMS is thought to give relief from insect bites, especially bull-ant bites.

BRACKEN FROND MATTRESSES were made by early settlers and drovers for camping.

Fungi
— hard at work

Above: Mycena clarkeana.

Kingdom: Fungi

Fungi form a huge group of organisms, with their own Kingdom. Fungi do not have leaves, stems or roots. They can live without oxygen and need no light as they don't manufacture food. Most fungi have a multi-celled body (mycelium), which is a network of microscopic threads (hyphae). A mycelium acts to find and process food and to produce fruit. Many fungi live a life underground, or hidden in debris, until perfect conditions occur, and we see the fruiting body emerge.

the FACTS!

OVER ONE MILLION SPECIES of fungi are thought to exist globally. Australia has well over 150,000 species, although fewer than 5% have been scientifically described.

PARTNERSHIP with underground fungi is the way of life for more than 75% of the world's plants.

ALMOST EVERY COLOUR of fungus occurs, though rarely green — they don't need the chlorophyll of green plants to make their food.

FUNGAL SHAPES are extraordinary. Some are like table tennis bats, or parachutes, umbrellas, jellyfish, starfish, brains, caps, lawyers' wigs, icicles, curtains, fans, coral or stars.

FUNKY FUNGUS NAMES include Punk, Skinhead, Beef Steak, Bread, Yellow Navel, Hairy Trumpet, Pancake Stack and Puff Ball.

THE GILLS OF one mushroom may hold many millions of microscopic spores. The fruit of a fungus expels spores for reproduction of the species. Spores are carried away by wind, water, insects, birds and animals to begin a new life.

Right: Golden Curtain Crust (*Stereum ostrea*) lives on stumps and fallen trees and can be found fruiting at any time of the year in rainforests around the east coast from northern Queensland to Victoria and Tasmania.

ALL HABITATS in Australia, from the coast to alpine areas, support fungal life. Fungi appear in the desert after good rain. In northern Australia fungi appear in warm rainforests during the wet season; in temperate areas the main season is March until July. You might even find some popping up in your garden.

Right: At night in southern Australian forests you may see an eerie green light. The poisonous Ghost Fungus (*Omphalotus nidiformis*) makes a luminous glow, caused by a chemical reaction between fungal enzymes and oxygen. *Below:* A species of *Geastrum*.

GREG HARM

NATURE'S RECYCLERS

Fungi have such an important role. They help each plant habitat maintain a finely balanced ecosystem. All Australian forests have a thick mat of fungal underlay beneath the soil. Rainforests and tall eucalypt forests provide dark damp places with lots of plant litter such as fallen trees, old stumps and leaves. Fungi decompose this organic matter really quickly by smothering it with strong acids to recycle it into nutrients for themselves and other plants. Some fungi even recycle the dead bodies of insects and animals, and others prefer animal droppings.

KEN STEPNELL/SP

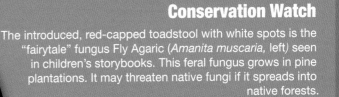

Below, left to right: Boletellus emotensis; Starfish or Anemone Fungus (Aseroe rubra) a type of fly-attracting stinkhorn.

RIGHT: GREG HARM

the FACTS!

THE ANTIBIOTIC PENICILLIN is made from a fungus, *Penicillium chrysogenum*. This fungus has saved many human lives.

YEAST IS A FRIENDLY FUNGUS used all over the world for bread, cheese, beer and wine making. Yeast is a single-celled organism.

TINEA, RINGWORM and dandruff are parasitic fungi that depend on humans and other animals for their survival. Damp, dark toe spaces are perfect for foot fungi to make tinea.

WALLABIES, POTOROOS (below) and bettongs sniff out, dig up and snack on truffle-like fungi as one of their favourite foods.

HORSE DROPPING FUNGUS, a *Pisolithus* species, is eaten by the Pintupi and Anmatjirra Aborigines of Central Australia.

INDIGENOUS PEOPLE of south–east Australia eat Native Bread (*Laccocephalum mylittae*), which fruits after bushfires. When the ground suddenly pushed upwards, they would dig up a soccer ball-sized treat that looks like bread and, some say, tastes like boiled rice.

HOMESICK FOREST

Over one million hectares of Australian eucalypts are grown in China, mainly for timber. Early plantations wouldn't grow as fast as they do in Australia. What was wrong? In Australia, eucalypts have a special partnership with ectomycorrhizal fungi. These fungi provide water and nutrients to the trees and in return the trees give fungi carbon. Eucalypt seedlings in China were inoculated with spore and they began to grow twice as quickly.

PONGS AND PERFUME

Fungi smells can be sweet or sour, great or gross. Many humans love the smell of the edible mushroom, *Agaricus campestris*. Wrinkled Cage (*Ileodictyon cibarium*) found in native forests of southern Australia looks like a white hollow soccer ball and smells like cheese or sour milk. Stinky smells of rotting meat are a trick used by stinkhorn fungus species to attract flies.

Beware of Splitgill (*Schizophyllum commune*), a very common white fan-shaped fungus, which grows on deadwood. It is thought that the disease basidioneuromycosis can be caught by accidentally sniffing up the spores while smelling its odour.

Goodenias
— primrose look-alikes

Family: Goodeniaceae
Genus: Goodenia

There are 181 species of Goodenia in the world and 176 of these are endemic to Australia. All but a few species have dainty, frilly yellow flowers, reminding people of the little native primroses of Europe. White, pink, blue and mauve are unusual colours for this genus. Each flower has five petals: two on the top, like ears, and three spread like a skirt on the bottom. A tiny cup on the tip of the style holds pollen until the flower opens, allowing insect pollinators to collect the pollen. Native Primrose (Goodenia lanata) is a yellow-flowered, trailing herb with a widespread distribution, found in open dry forests of New South Wales, Victoria and Tasmania.

Above: White Goodenia (*Goodenia scapigera*) is a white-flowered perennial herb found growing in sandy heathlands in places like Israelite Bay, the Stirling Ranges and Hyden in Western Australia.

the FACTS!

HAIRY GOODENIA (*Goodenia lunata*) was used in several ways by Indigenous people of Central Australia. One of Australia's early European botanists, FM Bailey, reported that Aborigines were able to settle their upset babies by giving them herbal medicine made from this plant. Also, because an extract in the plant acted like a tranquilliser, plants were thrown into small billabongs — making it easier to capture animals that came to drink.

INDIGENOUS TASMANIANS used to drink a medicine for diabetes made from infusing the leaves and stems of Hop Goodenia in water.

EARLY IRISH SETTLERS to the Wollongong area of New South Wales had a belief that if you walked through "Hunger Weed" as they called Hop Goodenia, (below) you would get a good appetite.

RARE GRASSHOPPERS SURVIVE

CSIRO scientists located a population of rare *Petasida ephippigera* grasshoppers in the Northern Territory. Live specimens, kept for observation and breeding purposes, were fed on foliage collected from Hop Goodenia growing in the Australian National Botanic Gardens. Hop Goodenia (*Goodenia ovata*) is widely distributed in temperate areas of Queensland, New South Wales, Victoria, Tasmania and South Australia.

Left: Leichhardt's Grasshopper (*Petasida epippigera*).

Below, left: Hop Goodenia (*Goodenia ovata*).

Below: Ivy Goodenia (*Goodenia hederacea*).

Grass-trees
— spiky & spear like

Family: Xanthorrhoeaceae
Genera: Xanthorrhoea & Kingia

All the world's 28 species of grass-trees in the Xanthorrhoea genus belong to Australia. They are closely related to the lily family. Grass-trees have been part of the Australian landscape for around 200 million years, surviving life with the dinosaurs and many dramatic environmental changes; and the lucky ones have been able to avoid destruction by humans. Grass-trees have the amazing ability to survive wild bush fires thanks to a fireproof jacket that protects the centuries-old trunk from being killed. Many living creatures, such as lizards, birds, and insects, depend on these unique plants for food and shelter. In South Australia the endangered Yellow-tailed Black Cockatoos feast on insect larvae in the flowering stalks. A study has recorded an amazing use of grass-trees by over 315 invertebrates and 100 vertebrates.

CATHY HOPE

Above: Western Australia's grass-tree (*Kingia australis*) has drum-stick-shaped flowers.

A VERY USEFUL PLANT

Flowers were sucked for the nectar and a sweet, citrus-flavoured drink was made by soaking flower stalks in water. Seeds were collected and ground into flour to make a type of cake. Nutty tasting, high energy food also came from the white bottoms of young inner leaves, the core of the stem and succulent roots. Delicious grubs could be found at the base of the plant. Spears were made from dried flower spikes and tough leaves were sharp enough to cut meat. When Aborigines needed to let others know where to find them, they set fire to a grass-tree as a signalling device.

Right: **Coastal grass-tree flower.**

the FACTS!

SOME GRASS-TREES in Australia are thought to be more than 600 years of age, making them some of the longest living plants on earth. Each metre of the trunk represents one hundred years.

"CRAMPY WAMPS" is the name given to a nervous system disease of cattle that have eaten grass-trees.

FIRST FLEET DOCTORS, on the eleven ships which arrived in Australia in January 1788, used diluted gum from grass-trees for a dysentery medicine.

EARLY SETTLERS used gum for varnish and shellac, picric acid (used in the manufacture of explosives), gas, tar, stove polish and coke.

SUPERGLUE OF THE BUSH

An archaeological dig conducted at Mt. Mulligan near Cairns, unearthed stone tools that are at least 3000 years old. Traces of glue attached to the tools were analysed and found to be from *Xanthorrhoea johnsonii*, which grows in this part of Queensland. Globules of strong-smelling gum ooze from the base of grass-trees and set rock-hard. This resin, which has had widespread use in Aboriginal technology for thousands of years, was traditionally melted by fire and used as a "super glue" to attach stone axes and spearheads. Being waterproof, the resin was also valued for coating bark canoes and wooden water-carrying containers.

Left: Xanthorrhoea australis in the Grampians National Park, Victoria.

Grasses
— feeding the world

Above: Kangaroos grazing. Expansion of grassland and installation of bores and water troughs across much of the Australian continent has allowed wallabies and kangaroos to thrive.

Right: Emus eat grasses, leaves, fruits, seeds and insects.

Family: Poaceae

Grasses belong to Poaceae, *the most important plant family for human society. With about 9000 species in the world and over 700 species in Australia, most food for the world's humans comes from grain-producing grasses such as rice, wheat, maize, oats, barley and rye. Grass is also on the menu for domesticated animals such as cattle, horses, sheep and goats.*

MANY WILD ANIMALS depend on grasses too, so healthy tussock grassland habitats are vital for their survival. Many native grasses of Australia are highly nutritious, have adapted to poor soils, have a high drought tolerance with permanent deep root systems and tend to thrive on being burnt every so often. Kangaroo Grass (*Themeda triandra*) is an extremely common native grass found in every State and Territory from alpine to arid habitats.

the FACTS!

NATIVE GRASSLANDS used to cover over one-third of Victoria. Sadly, more than 95% have disappeared.

NATIVE LEMON GRASS is represented in Australia by ten species. *Cymbopogon ambiguus* has the strongest scent, and Aboriginal people crush the leaves to inhale the vapour for chest and sinus complaints.

NUTRITIOUS BREAD is made by Aboriginal women who winnow grass seeds then ground them into flour. Woollybutt Grass (*Eragrostis eriopoda*) has a higher protein content than wholemeal wheat.

ABORIGINAL CHILDREN use grass stems to make play spears.

WRECKS OF SAILING SHIPS lie around the coastline of King Island. Long ago, pillows and mattresses stuffed with different types of grasses washed onto the shore. Seeds from the grasses escaped and began to grow amongst native grasses. The delicious cheeses and beef produced on King Island are attributed to the amazing mix of grasses for stock to graze on.

TANNINS FROM BUTTON GRASS (*Gymnoschoenus sphaerocephalus*) in Tasmania stain the rivers brown.

WILD RICE

Grasslands of the Top End floodplains in the Northern Territory are dominated by native wild rice (*Oryza* species), and it is here that some of the world's largest populations exist. Rice we can buy to eat is the cultivated rice *Oryza sativa*, a native of South-East Asia, and is the rice eaten by half of the people on earth. Australia has four species belonging to the *Oryza* genus and Roly–Poly (*Oryza meridionalis*) is known to have been an important food grain for Aboriginal people of the Gulf of Carpentaria. Their name for wild rice is Mukumardu. Many thousands of Magpie Geese (below) depend on wild rice as a vital food source.

MARTIN WILLIS

SPINIFEX — SURVIVES AND THRIVES

Above, top to bottom: Spinifex hummock showing flower and seed stalks; Spinifex Hopping-mouse.

Tasmania is the only State in Australia without any of the 64 species of spinifex grasses that predominate in more than one-fifth of the continent.

Australia's worst soils and most arid areas host spinifex, which has evolved and adapted enough to survive, and even thrive, here. Roots may reach down ten metres deep, and will also spread out widely in search of moisture. Needle-sharp leaves start life flat, then curl into thin, tight prickly cylinders which discourage large herbivorous animals from grazing. The Euro and Rufous Hare-Wallaby will eat spinifex — despite its low nutritional value — in the absence of other, more palatable native grasses. Bilby colonies coexist with spinifex, because they eat the termites which are spinifex grazers. Their burrows are protected because spinifex spines deter hunting animals. Spinifex Hopping-mice also dig their burrows near spinifex.

In Central Australia, Indigenous children have fun in the dark, lighting bundles of green spinifex. The resin in the leaves explodes like sparklers as it burns.

Above: Hard Spinifex or Porcupine Grass (*Triodia basedowii*). After maturing, the rounded hummocks begin to die out from the centre, leaving rings.

CARTWHEELING COASTAL GRASS

Nature has given Hairy Spinifex (*Spinifex hirsutus*, below) two clever ways to reproduce. Tough rhizomes send out new plants which spread rapidly, binding sand and preventing dune erosion. In addition, wind spins cartwheeling female seed heads over and over, to disperse seeds as they tumble along.

the FACTS!

CULTIVARS of suitable native grasses are being developed for sustainable farming in Australia.

ABORIGINAL TECHNOLOGY has benefitted from the black resinous substance found at the base of Soft Spinifex (*Triodia pungens*). It provides a strong cement to secure spearheads to spears and stone axe heads to wooden handles. On hot days resin drips down the spiky stems to gather at the base.

THE MITCHELL GRASS DOWNS are a recognised "ecoregion" of tropical semi-arid north-western Qld and north-eastern NT. *Astrebla* genus grasses grow on cracking black clay soils, which provide crevices for animal populations.

Grevilleas
— a gardener's favourite

Family: Proteaceae
Genus: Grevillea

Above, top to bottom: A range of grevillea flower shapes.

Grevillea *species, often called "Spider Flowers" are popular in Australian gardens for their incredible range of varieties.* Grevillea *is the third largest genus in Australia with over 350 species. These species have showy, bird-attracting inflorescences (blooms) that glisten with nectar. Most blooms have up to a hundred or more tiny flowers artistically arranged in shapes described as spider, toothbrush, comb and bottlebrush. Leaves are also extremely diverse, ranging from fern, to feather, holly, star, rush and pine needle shapes.*

Above: The tiny, 10 g Eastern Spinebill extracting nectar from grevillea flowers.

NECTAR ROBBERS

During the evolutionary process, grevillea flower shapes adapted to suit nectar-seeking birds, not bees. Flowers feature a barrier of hairs inside them, to prevent the small Australian native bees reaching the nectar. Since the larger, introduced bees have entered Australia, they have robbed nectar by pushing their way through the barrier of hairs. They steal nectar which is intended for birds and interrupt the fertilisation of the plant.

Above: A Scaly-breasted Lorikeet taking nectar from a grevillea.

the FACTS!

TENS OF MILLIONS OF YEARS ago, nectar-feeding honeyeaters evolved along with the flowering plants of the Proteaceae family, which includes grevilleas. The two needed each other for survival.

A NEW HOLLAND HONEYEATER takes nectar from fifteen to 100 flowers per minute. Honeyeaters have curved beaks and brush-tipped tongues.

NATURE ORGANISED most grevillea flowers in shades of pink, red, apricot, orange, yellow and gold to match the needs of nectar-feeding birds like the honeyeaters. It's thought that red and yellow are the colours best seen by birds.

FRIARBIRDS, named after Friar monks, have evolved a bald patch on their head. This adaptation prevents feathers getting sticky from nectar and pollen. Little Friarbirds and Silver-crowned Friarbirds take nectar from Fern-leafed Grevillea (*Grevillea pteridifolia*) in places like Kakadu, on the seasonally flooded grassy flats.

POLLEN PRESENTERS

Each grevillea bud is a power-packed flower package. The developing female part of the flower, a very long style, is tightly curled up with its stigma firmly held between the two sets of pollen producing male organs, the anthers. When the flower is ready to open, tension within the style causes it to uncurl, and the pollen-dusted stigma breaks free from the anthers. The curved style springs into position so its stigma acts as a pollen presenter, taking a male role, to dab pollen on the head of any nectar-seeking bird. Then the stigma reverts to a female role and becomes quite sticky and ready to be fertilised by pollen, which arrives from other flowers on the heads of birds.

Above: Pitjantjatjara people of Central Australia collect the dry seed pods from Rattlepod Grevillea (*Grevillea stenobotrya*), shaking them as a musical instrument when they are performing a ceremonial dance.

FIX-IT GUM

Warlpiri people, in their traditional life, sometimes made cement to repair their tools, using red gum from Beefwood (*Grevillea striata*). After collecting the gum, it was heated and mixed with kangaroo dung. Indigenous people believed in the healing powers of Beefwood gum, which was diluted in water to apply to burns and sores.

STANLEY BREEDEN

Left: Anangu children of Uluru in central Australia love sucking the sweet nectar from Honey Grevillea (*Grevillea eriostachya*).

the FACTS!

TIMBER FROM BEEFWOOD (*Grevillea striata*), was split and used for roof shingles by early settlers. This timber is still used for fence posts. Beefwood grows in Northern Australia and is known in the Ross River region. Cattle graze on the foliage of Beefwood.

"SPIDERMAN" GREVILLEA is much sought after as a cut flower, and is grown on a large scale in Israel for the European market.

SOUTHERN SILKY OAK, (*Grevillea robusta*) Australia's tallest grevillea, is plantation grown in South Africa.

CSIRO SCIENTISTS have found that grevillea seeds have a high concentration of mineral nutrients even though they grow in poor soils. Indigenous people in Central Australia have known for thousands of years that the seeds of some *Grevillea* species can be eaten raw.

GREVILLEA "SEEDBANKS"

Ants assist between one-third and half of all Australian native plants to propagate. Seed from the *Grevillea* genus is dragged by worker ants into underground nests and they eat the fleshy appendages, called elaiosomes, on the seeds. By doing this, the ants are helping ensure the future of the plants, by safely storing seeds underground in a "seedbank". Soon after bushfires have swept through a grevillea habitat, seedlings of the grevillea emerge, often from an ant's nest. Ants are often observed carrying away the sticky seed pods and seeds of Dryander's Grevillea (*Grevillea dryandri*) of WA and NT.

Right: Dryander's Grevillea (*Grevillea dryandri*).

Gum Trees
— fragrant national icon

Family: Myrtaceae
Genera: Eucalyptus, Corymbia & Angophora

The gum tree is a symbol of Australia, showing superb adaptation to a wide range of climates and conditions in all corners of the continent. Eucalypts made Australia home millions of years ago, by successfully colonising suitable habitats and developing features to help them tolerate floods, fire, drought and poor soils. Australia has approximately 850 eucalypt species with many diverse groups including Bloodwoods, Stringybarks, Box Gums and Peppermints. Some species are widely distributed and represented in different habitats. Others have a restricted distribution and some are endangered species. Eucalypts are found at the coast, up to the snowline in high alpine areas, spread out over the plains and into the arid inland.

Above: Tasmanian Blue Gum blossom.

Right: The eucalpyts thrive in a wide range of climate zones, from arid to alpine.

the FACTS!

ANTARCTICA HAS GIVEN US fossilised pollen from the extremely old plant family Myrtaceae, to which eucalypts belong. Australia has 1645 of the world's 3000 species in this family.

DNA RESEARCH tells us that the ancestors of today's eucalypts developed about 70 million years ago in moist rainforests.

91 EUCALYPT SPECIES are found in the Greater Blue Mountains region. This area is thought to be the place where eucalypts first evolved.

FOSSILISED EUCALYPT LEAVES from the Tertiary period found in south-west Australia, and pollen from the Torrens Basin in Central Australia, have been dated at 45 million years of age.

EUCALYPTUS CURTISII, a bloodwood of south–eastern Queensland, is Australia's most primitive eucalypt.

FLORAL EMBLEM

Tasmanian Blue Gum (*Eucalyptus globulus*) is Tasmania's floral emblem. These tall forest trees are native to the east coast of Tasmania, King and Flinders Islands and the Otway Ranges and Wilson's Promontory in Victoria.

Over 450,000 hectares of Tasmanian Blue Gums are growing in plantations on land that used to grow crops and pasture. This fast growing hardwood is suitable for timber and pulp production. Remnant vegetation is included in some of these plantings. Blue gums will not thrive in arid areas and must have an annual rainfall of more than 600 mm. Tasmanian Blue Gums in coastal areas of California have been grown there for over one hundred years, and many people mistake them for Californian native trees.

Above, left to right: Red-flowering Gum (*E. ficifolia*); Mottlecah (*E. macrocarpa*); Lemon-flowered Mallee (*E. woodwardii*).

HIGHRISE LIVING

River Red Gum (*Eucalyptus camaldulensis*) is the most widely distributed gum tree in Australia and is found anywhere there is a waterway or old riverbed. River Red Gums' survival is dependent on a flood every so often.

Barmah Forest beside the Murray River on the Victoria–New South Wales border is the biggest native forest of River Red Gums in the world. Some of the trees are over 40 m high and 500 years old. These tall gum trees are especially suited to highrise living, they are the apartment blocks of the river. Roots growing in the water offer basement living for small fish and frogs. Exposed roots provide perches for cormorants and other birds as they wait for fish to appear. Leaves are homes for aphids, lerps, saw-flies and numerous caterpillars. Bark is a hideaway for ladybirds, beetles, insects and lizards. Rosellas, cockatoos, galahs, owls and kookaburras nest in hollows, which also make good hives for native bees to store honey. Flocks of Little Corellas rest on branches. But kites and eagles have the penthouse positions, their nests are the highest homes.

Above: River Red Gums on the Ovens River, Victoria.

Above: Marri (*Corymbia calophylla*).

the FACTS!

MOTTLECAH (*Eucalyptus macrocarpa*) has a flower the size of a small ball. It's the largest flower of any gum tree.

EVERY GUM NUT has a cap called an operculum. The blossom is tucked inside the gum nut until the force of hundreds of stamens pop the cap off (below).

BEES MAKE DELICIOUS HONEY from the nectar of many species of gum blossom, such as Yellow Box, Red Gum, Mallee and Sugar Gum.

BEES, BUTTERFLIES and birds take nectar from gum blossoms during the day. At night, possums and flying-foxes have a turn.

ANIMAL VISITORS GET DUSTED with pollen and, without realising it, do the tree a favour by transferring the pollen to another flowering gum tree for fertilisation.

MALARIA CONTROL

Over a hundred years ago many trees of Tasmanian Blue Gum (*Eucalyptus globulus*) and River Red Gum (*Eucalyptus camaldulensis,* below) were planted in marshes of Italy and Israel to drain water that attracts mosquitoes and breeds malaria. River Red Gum's species name comes from the town Camalduli in Italy.

Above: Bushfires are a major force in the evolution of eucalypts.

Left: The oil citronellal, from Lemon Scented Gum (*Corymbia citriodora*) is used in mosquito repellent and in the perfume industry. Plantations of Australia's Lemon Scented Gum are grown in India, South Africa and Fiji.

EUCALYPTUS OIL PRODUCTION

Eucalyptus oil is extracted from gum leaves and is used for medicinal products such as antiseptics, inhalants, gargles, cough mixture and cough lollies. Paint, disinfectant and cleaning products also use this oil. It's an environmentally friendly industrial solvent.

Production of oil has declined in Australia over the years from 1000 tonnes of oil in 1947 to about 100 tonnes per year. Most eucalyptus oil produced in Australia today comes from Blue Mallee Gum (*Eucalyptus polybractea*).

Currently, 90% of Australia's demand for eucalyptus oil comes from China, South Africa and Brazil. *Eucalyptus globulus* is the main tree grown overseas for oil production. Worldwide production of oil distilled from Australia's eucalypts is about 4000 tonnes. China, the world's largest producer of eucalyptus oil, distills it as a timber industry by-product.

EUCALYPTUS OIL POWER

Australia has some challenging and promising projects on the go — mass plantings of gum trees aim to mitigate global warming and farmland salinity.

In Western Australia's wheat belt, farmers are planting two million mallee gums (once cleared as an agricultural pest) to provide power for 1000 homes. The power is to be processed at Narrogin. Electricity will be generated from coppiced mallee wood and leaves, with oil and activated carbon as by-products. Plans for five such future power stations will require 20 million more mallee gums.

BLUE HILLS

What makes Australia's hills look blue from a distance? As a gum tree transpires in the heat of the day, water vapour — along with tiny droplets of eucalyptus oil — escapes from the stomata in the leaves. As the eucalyptus oil floats above the forest in the earth's atmosphere, the rays of the sun hit the droplets and refract back to our eyes as blue. The hotter the day, the more the plant transpires and the deeper the blue of the hills. The Blue Mountains area is a centre of diversity for gum trees. This phenomenon, described in 1911, is called Rayleigh's Scattering.

the FACTS!

EUCALYPT LEAVES have a high oil content, and catch fire very easily.

BUSHFIRES determine the health of the natural environment in many parts of Australia and are a major factor in the evolution of a diverse range of eucalypts.

MANY EUCALYPT species have adapted to fire and can rapidly regenerate soon after a fire has swept through the forest.

AS EUCALYPTS GROW, most develop a form of protection to give them a chance to recover after fire. Lignotubers are like underground "bushfire shelters" containing food reserves and little buds that can spring to life with the help of rain.

WHEN REGROWTH occurs after a fire many eucalyptus tree trunks seem to be clothed in foliage. New shoots grow from epicormic buds.

BIG THINGS FROM SMALL THINGS GROW

Mountain Ash (*Eucalyptus regnans*) is the world's tallest flowering plant, growing up to 100 m. Some giants felled years ago may have been 120 m high. It is also amazing to know that this tree grows from one of the world's smallest seeds.

Tasmania and Victoria have stunning natural forests of Mountain Ash, and New Zealand is growing large plantations of the tree.

Mountain Ash trees depend on a bush fire to help them reproduce. Heat cracks the gum nuts open and the tiny seeds fall to the forest floor to begin growing. Fire kills the trees as they do not have the re-sprouting ability of most other gums.

During severe drought conditions you can listen to a Mountain Ash with a stethoscope. If it is very stressed due to lack of water, you will hear clicking noises inside the trunk. A tree will sacrifice a limb to save its body when it is under serious stress such as during a drought.

GREG HARM/SFP

the FACTS!

30 MILLION HECTARES of gum trees planted today would produce enough methanol and ethanol in 50 years time to fuel our vehicles.

MORE THAN 108 COUNTRIES have eucalypt plantations, totalling more than 13 million hectares. The biggest growers are India (with over 2,500,000 hectares) and China (with nearly 700,000 hectares).

NEW ZEALAND grows plantations of several Eucalypt hardwoods.

SPAIN AND SOUTH AFRICA grow Australian gum trees to supply Italy with pulp for its rayon industry.

CLEAR CELLOPHANE paper is made from gum tree pulp.

PARTICLE BOARD for building furniture, cupboards and flooring can be made from waste chips of timber from gum trees. Egypt and Brazil produce particle board from their Australian gum tree plantations.

THE SAP that oozes like blood from injured gum trees is called kino. This sticky sap is an acidic, astringent compound that contains tannin used for tanning leather. Brown Mallet (*Eucalyptus astringens*) from the south-west of Western Australia is an important source of tannin.

MONEY GROWS ON TREES

Estimates say that two million tonnes of CO_2 could be absorbed from the atmosphere every year by 100,000 hectares of trees in young plantations. Some Australian landowners are having eucalypt trees planted and are being paid carbon credits for the carbon sequestration (capturing) service provided by the trees. They are being encouraged to rent out some land for plantations — and for a steady income.

OVER 400 SPECIES of Australia's eucalypts were planted at Mt Annan Native Botanic Garden, in New South Wales, as a bicentennial project for 1988. Try growing your own local eucalypt species! Sow seeds during any season in warm areas. Sprinkle seed in moist, sandy soil. Add wildflower seed starter, which contains a smoke chemical to assist germination. Seedlings should appear within 15 to 21 days.

Right: Yellow-flowering Gum, Northern Territory.

Above: The graceful, hardy Ghost Gum always contrasts beautifully with its vivid environment.

"Once a jolly swagman camped by a billabong, Under the shade of a Coolabah tree"

WALTZING MATILDA TREE

The Coolabah tree was made famous in A.B Paterson's famous song Waltzing Matilda. Coolabahs (*Eucalyptus coolabah*) are found beside billabongs, lakes and rivers in places such as Alice Springs and Katherine in the Northern Territory, the Murchison River in Western Australia, Lake Eyre in South Australia and Narrabri in New South Wales.

ANOTHER FAMOUS COOLABAH TREE
(*Eucalyptus microtheca*) is the "Dig Tree" (right) at Cooper's Creek. Supplies of food were buried at the base of this tree during Burke and Wills' 1860 expedition to north Australia. Plantations of Coolabah trees are grown in South Africa, mostly for firewood.

GHOST GUMS

Ghost gums (*Corymbia aparrerinja*), feature in the landscape of arid Australia. Their trunks are stark white. A powdery covering that is a sunscreen protects the tree from extremely hot days. Aborigines have used this white dust to whiten their headbands for ceremonial dress. Aboriginal artist Albert Namatjira often featured Ghost Gums in his central Australian landscapes.

the FACTS!

INDIGENOUS AUSTRALIANS use of gum trees has been extensive. Fine strands of bark make string for "string figures". Bark is also used for shelters, shields, paintings, canoes and containers.

WOOD MAKES SPEARS, clap-sticks, clubs, spear-throwers, smoking pipes and containers.

THE ANANGU PEOPLE of Central Australia collect a white flaky crust called lerp (the cover of an nymph-stage insect) from the underside of gum leaves. They roll it into a ball and eat it as a lolly.

MESSMATE STRINGYBARK (*Eucalyptus obliqua*) has inner bark that makes string for nets and bags.

THE SAP of River Red Gum was used by Indigenous leader Barak of the Yarra people in Vic as an ointment for burns and other skin problems. A gargle for sore throats was made by mixing sap with water.

SAP WAS ALSO used as a fixative to mix with ochres for paintings.

CALENDAR TREES

When the Aborigines of the Top End see the bright orange gum blossom of Darwin Woollybutt (*Eucalyptus miniata*) in May, they know the dry season "Wurrgeng" has begun. It also indicates that they need to begin their firestick burning. Aborigines have six seasons in the Top End.

Didgeridoos are made from Darwin Woollybutt trunks that have been hollowed out by termites. In Arnhem Land the bark from this tree is soaked in water to make a medicine for diarrhoea.

Above: The beautiful flowers of Darwin Woollybutt.

Right: A didgeridoo. Termites are the most important grazers and recyclers on Australian grasslands — and their crafting of musical instruments for people is a fortunate by-product.

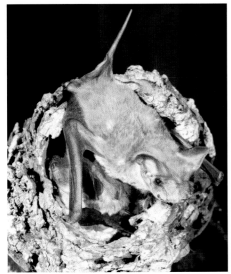

HOME AMONG THE GUM TREES

The leaves of Manna Gum (*Eucalyptus viminalis*) provide a "live-in" restaurant for koalas — and the drink is provided too. Tender young leaves supply most of the moisture a koala needs. Gum leaves are not very nutritious, so hundreds have to be eaten every day to give the koala strength to be active for a short time at night. Up to 20 hours of their day is spent huddled up asleep in the fork of a tree.

At Springton in South Australia there is a famous 500-year-old gum tree. A pioneer German family set up home in the Herbig Tree, where they lived in the base of the trunk with the first two of their sixteen children.

GREG HARM/SPP

Below, left to right: Most gum leaves are long, narrow, thin and pointed; Some are like a curved blade and others rounded; Young trees of some species begin with round leaves then change to long leaves.

Top and left: Many Australian birds, bees and marsupials depend on finding nesting hollows in mature eucalypts.

CENTRE: MICHAEL CERMAK

the FACTS!

A GUM LEAF makes a good band-aid. Eucalyptus oil gives the leaf an antiseptic quality.

MUSIC CAN BE MADE by blowing on a gum leaf. There are even gum-leaf-playing competitions.

THE THIN BLADE of the leaf turns to face the sun during extreme heat, to reduce evaporation.

SNOW GUMS have tough leaves with waxy white coatings to cope with extreme cold. The oil inside the leaf acts as an antifreeze.

GUM LEAVES hang down to allow as much light as possible through the tree to the forest floor and to guide falling rain to the ground.

EACH GUM SPECIES has a slightly different smell. Crush a leaf to release and smell the unique eucalyptus fragrance.

Above: Conspicuous bright yellow markings on the green leaves of Wavy-leaved Hakea (*Hakea undulata*), display an intricate network of veins.

Hakeas
— southern belles

Family: Proteaceae
Genus: Hakea

The Hakea *genus, with 149 species, is endemic to Australia. It's estimated that south-west Australia has 65% of these plants.* Hakea *species are sometimes described as "Corkwoods" due to the thick, cracked and wrinkled bark on the trunks of many species.*

the FACTS!

PREVENTION OF BROWSING by megafauna may be the reason that many *Hakea* species evolved extremely tough, spiky and sometimes "needle–sharp" leaves.

MIMICRY is also a form of defence for this species. Scary-looking "bullet proof" fruits evolved to turn predators away. Some are covered with wart-like knobs, some mimic insect homes and some have "caterpillar–like" horns. The woody spotted fruit of Frog Hakea (*Hakea nitida*) growing in the Ravensthorpe region of Western Australia, even looks like a frog.

HAKEA PLATYSPERMA has huge round fruit just like cricket balls and the fruit of *Hakea petiolaris* is shaped like a sea urchin.

Above: Scallops Hakea (*Hakea cucullata*) grows in sand or gravel in Western Australia, south to Albany and east to Cape Riche. Cup-like or scallop-shell-like leaves cradle the flowers.

THESE EXTREMELY hardy plants are heat, drought and frost tolerant. Some can withstand a fire and regenerate growth from lignotubers, which are water-bearing, swollen rootstock. Many *Hakeas* depend on fire — to split open their tough fruit cases, and to release two winged seeds. *Hakea* flowers are at times confused with *Grevilleas*. Red Pokers (*Hakea bucculenta*) is a most attractive tree growing up to seven metres tall. It's found between Shark Bay and Mingenew in Western Australia.

FANTASTIC FOLIAGE

The most striking feature about Royal Hakea (*Hakea victoria,* above), is the way it dominates the landscape, like frilled totem poles with fantastic red, green and yellow foliage. Leaves live for up to five years, becoming more colourful as they age. It has also been observed that the poorer the soil, the brighter the foliage becomes. Royal Hakea is also known as, "Chinese Lantern Bush" in Western Australia's Ravensthorpe area, where it grows on heathland in Fitzgerald National Park.

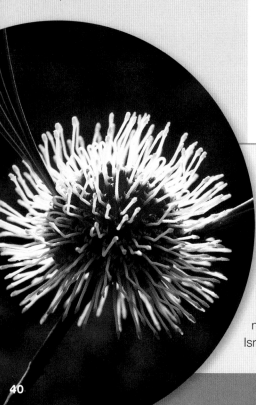

PIN CUSHIONS

Flowers of Pin-cushion Hakea (*Hakea laurina*), probably the best known *Hakea* species in Australia, provide nectar for the long-snouted Honey Possum (*Tarsipes rostratus*). In return this tiny possum assists the plant with pollination. This plant species grows naturally between Narrogin, Albany and Israelite Bay in Western Australia.

Conservation Watch

Kangaroo Island has an extremely mysterious and rare hakea that doesn't set seeds and can only reproduce from underground suckers. Amazingly, Enigma Hakea (*Hakea aenigma*), has managed to spread out over an area of 30 km by 15 km.

GROWING HAKEAS

Hakea seeds are easy to grow and will take 3–6 weeks to germinate.

Two-winged seeds sit in each woody fruit. They can be released by placing the fruit in a dry paper bag on a sunny windowsill. Plant the seed, with the wings slightly exposed, in a pot of moist sandy soil and cover them with a plastic bag, removing it when germination occurs.

Hakea seed wholesalers have estimated that having enough seed from one species would make it worth $5000 per kg.

Burrendong Arboretum in New South Wales has many species under cultivation in a "Hakea Walk".

Eco-sourcing for the garden means getting plants grown from local seed and has many benefits. It protects the character of regional ecosystems, protects local gene diversity, and should produce plants that are preadapted to the soils and climate.

Left and above: During Matthew Flinders' 1801 "Investigator" expedition, botanist Robert Brown collected Harsh Hakea (*Hakea prostrata*) in south-western Australia.

the FACTS!

HAKEAS WERE TAKEN to England by sailing ship in the 1790s.

AUSTRALIA'S HAKEAS, *Hakea sericea* and *Hakea gibbosa* were taken to grow in South Africa long ago, and have now been declared noxious weeds in that country.

LIVES WERE SAVED when thirsty Aborigines and explorers found water in the swollen roots of Needlewood (*Hakea leucoptera*), which grows in all mainland States of Australia.

Heaths
— thriving in adversity

Family: Ericaceae
Genus: Epacris, Leucopogon, Richea, Sprengelia

Heath refers to both a type of vegetation and a group of plants. The Australian heaths belong to the Ericaceae — a mainly Northern Hemisphere family known for garden plants such as Rhododendron *and* Erica. *Heath plants grow in poor soils, so are usually of low height. Evergreen* Epacris *shrubs grow in a range of habitats from sea level to about 1000 metres, and are common in exposed heathland vegetation.*

Above: Fuchsia Heath (*Epacris longiflora*) grows to 1 m. It is native to NSW and Qld.

FLORAL EMBLEM

Victoria was the first State to select a floral emblem. Pink or Common Heath (*Epacris impressa*) brightens the bush in winter, adding "cheerfulness" when not many other species are flowering. Pink Heath comes in white, pale and deep pink and red and is native to Victoria, NSW, South Australia (including Kangaroo Island) and Tasmania. It has been cultivated in England for many years, being highly valued for the bright blooms it produces at Christmas, in the Northern Hemisphere's winter.

the FACTS!

OF 40 *EPACRIS* SPECIES in the world, 35 are native to Australia, and several endemic to New Zealand.

HUGE ADULT carrion flies are known to pollinate *Epacris* species.

THE SEED OF *EPACRIS* SPECIES has been found to germinate with more success if it has been kept in a dark, dry place for a few months.

CINNAMON FUNGUS is a serious plant disease that threatens some *Epacris* populations.

LARVAE of the Montane Heath-blue butterfly eat flowers of *Epacris breviflora*, *Epacris petrophila* and *Epacris paludosa*.

THREATENED SPECIES

Twelve species of *Epacris*, found only in Tasmania are classified as being either Vulnerable or Endangered. An Epacrid Recovery Plan was set up in 1999 to create awareness and make positive moves to ensure their survival. All twelve species are being cultivated at the Royal Tasmanian Botanic Gardens. Freycinet Heath (*Epacris barbata*) growing only on the Freycinet Peninsula is Critically Endangered.

Left: Tasmanian endemic, *Epacris virgata*.

Above: Blunt-leafed Heath (*Epacris obtusifolia*) grows in damp places in SA, Vic, NSW, Qld and Tas.

Conservation Watch

Unfortunately some of Australia's heaths are picked from the bush for use in the cut flower trade. In Western Australia this has happened to the beautiful pink *Leucopogon verticillatus*.

Above: Pink Swamp Heath (*Sprengelia incarnata*), is a small shrub growing to 1 m. Tiny pink star-shaped flowers are clustered on the end of stems.

LEUCOPOGON

Another large genus in the heath family is *Leucopogon,* with 230 species worldwide and about 200 in Australia. Most plants are small shrubs growing in coastal heathlands. Nearly all have small white flowers that are bearded, and quite a few have edible berries. Coastal Bearded Heath (*Leucopogon parviflorus,* left) is native to all coastal temperate areas of Australia and is very common along the Great Ocean Road in Victoria. It's also a native plant of New Zealand. Edible cream-coloured berries provide food for seagulls, silvereyes, fairy wrens and emus.

the FACTS!

THE WORLD'S LARGEST concentration of heath plants in the Ericaceae family is in Australia, which has 28 of the world's 31 heath genera and 356 of the world's 426 heath species.

COASTS AND ALPINE HABITATS are the places where heath plants are most often found. They grow in low shrublands. These heath areas make up about 6% of Australia.

DENSE VEGETATION is the norm in heath habitats. Compact shrubs protect each other from the wind.

HEATHLANDS PROVIDE HOMES for wombats, echnidas, reptiles, many birds, kangaroos and smaller marsupials such as the Southern Brown Bandicoot (below).

THE LARGEST HEATH IN THE WORLD

Australia has ten *Richea* species: nine in Tasmania and one in the mountains of New South Wales and Victoria. The world's largest heath belongs to the genus *Richea*. You could be tricked into thinking Pandani (*Richea pandanifolia*) is a tall palm tree or a grass-tree, but it's not. It's a heath that is endemic to Tasmania and normally grows to 12 m high in damp, mountain forests.

Above: Pandani growing on a hillside — some reach 18 m high.

Left: Low stature heath vegetation on sand.

Above: Orange Stars (*Hibbertia stellaris*).

Hibbertias
— Guinea Flowers

Family: Dilleniaceae
Genus: Hibbertia

The world has about 115 species of Hibbertia, *with most native to Australia. Other countries with* Hibbertia *include, Papua New Guinea, Fiji, Madagascar and New Caledonia. More than 60 of Australia's 110 species occur in South West Western Australia.* Hibbertias *are also known as Guinea Flowers. Almost every species has glowing, sunshine-yellow flowers ranging from 1–5 cm in diameter. Each flower has five heart-shaped petals, and some even look like buttercups.*

the FACTS!

ORANGE FLOWERS are unusual for *Hibbertia* species. Western Australian species, Orange Stars (*Hibbertia stellaris,* above), is a low-growing shrub covered with masses of orange flowers. Another beautiful orange flowering species in Western Australia is *Hibbertia miniata*.

KANGAROOS AND WALLABIES eat the fresh young foliage from some *Hibbertia* species.

TWO NATIVE BEES, Teddy Bear Bee and Blue Banded Bee, visit and "buzz pollinate" Twining Guinea Flower (*Hibbertia scandens*) and others.

INSECTS WITH ULTRAVIOLET vision probably see hibbertia flowers as two colours, the flowers can reflect ultraviolet radiation.

KAKADU AREA ABORIGINES have been known to use dried hibbertia branches as firesticks, for carrying fire.

HIBBERTIA SEEDS have seed coats with long dormancy ability. For seeds to germinate, a fire must sweep through the area.

SELF-PROPAGATION is a possibility for some prostrate *Hibbertia* species. They form cloned plants by layering on the ground.

THE PETALS on Yellow Buttercup (*Hibbertia hypericoides*) are a perfect heart shape. This plant is found in coastal areas and jarrah forests from Geraldton to Margaret River and is the most common plant growing in Whiteman Park near Perth.

Left: Yellow Buttercup (Hibbertia hypericoides).

Above, left to right: Almost all Guinea flowers have yellow heart-shaped petals.

WHICH DIRECTION?

Climbing Guinea Flower (*Hibbertia dentata*), with golden yellow flowers 5 cm across, is a vigorous climber found growing in sand dunes on the east coast of Australia. English naturalist, Charles Darwin (1809–1882) studied Australian plants to see how they climb. Some vines are programmed to twine in an anticlockwise direction and others do the opposite and twine clockwise, never changing. Charles Darwin also discovered that vines twine at a faster rate on a warm day.

Kangaroo Paws
— ambassadors abroad

Family: Haemodoraceae
Genus: Anigozanthos 11 species, Macropidia one species

Kangaroo Paws are boldly identifiable plants in Western Australia's bushland scenery. "Hands" of clasping, finger-like buds have given these plants their name. Stems and buds look like the dexterous, furry paws and curved nails of kangaroos. The velvety, six-petalled flowers delight people with brightest reds, greens, yellows and oranges, so these plants are in great demand outside Australia.

Above and left: Clumps of Cat's Paw (*Anigozanthos humilis*) are found growing in sandy open areas of the Jerdacuttup Plain west of Esperance. They are also common along road run-offs and firebreaks.

THE TUBULAR FLOWER shape is one of nature's clever adaptions, planned to brush pollen onto the heads of long-beaked nectar-feeding birds such as wattlebirds and honeyeaters. Tiny Honey Possums also help with pollination by feeding on the nectar. All Kangaroo Paws are perennial and, after spring flowering, the foliage of most plants withers back to survive as underground rhizomes — for protection during hot summers. The rhizomes provided food for Aborigines.

FLORAL EMBLEM

Mangle's Kangaroo Paw (*Anigozanthos manglesii*) is the most widespread Kangaroo Paw, found growing around the Perth district and almost as far north as Shark Bay. It is also WA's floral emblem. Distinctive flowers with the stop–start colours of red and green light up the bush wherever they grow.

Robert Mangles created a sensation in England during the 1830s when he grew these strange, novel plants from seed. By 1836 a British botanist David Don had named the plant *Anigozanthos manglesii*.

DURING THE EUROPEAN CHRISTMAS season, Red Kangaroo Paw (*A. rufus*) is highly sought-after as a cut flower. In 1792, Jacques-Julien Houton de Labillardière collected a specimen of Red Kangaroo Paw near Esperance. He was the first to collect this curious plant and take it to Europe.

the FACTS!

ALL TWELVE KANGAROO PAW species are endemic to Western Australia.

BLACK AND GREEN FLOWERS are extremely rare in nature. However, Black Kangaroo Paw (*Macropidia fuliginosa*) has this combination.

COMMERCIAL GROWERS for the cut flower industry grow between 6000–8000 plants per hectare.

94% OF JAPAN'S Kangaroo Paw demand is grown in Australia. During 1995, 4.3 million stems were exported to Japan, mainly from Western Australia and New South Wales. Some plantations are also grown in Japan.

SOUTH AMERICA, South Africa, the USA and Israel are growing Kangaroo Paw on a large scale.

KANGAROO PAWS are cloned in tissue culture laboratories. There are now about 100 different varieties.

Kunzeas
— wood & heath dwellers

Family: Myrtaceae
Genus: Kunzea

Kunzea species bloom in spring and summer with perfumed flowers that have a fluffy appearance caused by many very prominent stamens. Kunzea species grow mainly in coastal and mallee areas and vary from ground-huggers to shrubs 1–5 m high. Crimson Kunzea, (Kunzea baxteri, below), is loved by parrots for the nectar produced in the bright red bottlebrush flowers with gold-tipped stamens. It is widely cultivated as an attractive garden plant. Granite outcrops from Esperance to Israelite Bay support the growth of these plants.

Above: Kunzea ericoides.

the FACTS!

KUNZEA is an Australian genus (though one species extends to New Zealand). The approximately 42 species are in the Myrtaceae family, so are closely related to Bottlebrushes, Tea Trees, Gum Trees, Paperbarks and Feather Flowers.

WHITE KUNZEA (*Kunzea ambigua*) of Vic, NSW and Tas is also known as "Tick Bush", as it provides a haven for bandicoots hosting ticks.

KUNZEA ERICOIDES is causing concern because it successfully spreads and colonises bare land — so it may be declared a weed. This *Kunzea* species of Queensland, New South Wales, Australian Capital Territory and Victoria has blooms that look like "whiskered" white tea tree flowers.

EARLY SETTLERS used aromatic leaves of some *Kunzea* species to brew a tonic or a refreshing drink of tea.

KUNZEA SPECIES FLOWERS are full of nectar to attract birds and native bees to assist with pollination.

QUEENSLAND HAS five species with one very rare. *Kunzea calida* has ball-shaped purple flowers.

Above, top to bottom: Crimson Kunzea (*Kunzea baxterii);* Violet Kunzea, (*Kunzea parvifolia*); White Kunzea (*Kunzea ambigua*).

MUNTRIE MUNCHIES

In late summer, children on Kangaroo Island in South Australia snack on blueberry-sized berries called Muntries (below), from *Kunzea pomifera*, which carpet sand dunes and fill the air with an apple-orchard aroma. Some say they taste like dried Granny Smith apples, others say the taste is more a spicy apple taste.

For thousands of years Narrindjeri people of the Coorong feasted on the fresh berries, dried plenty to pound into powder for cake-making in winter and saved some for trading with other tribes.

Muntries are the fourth-largest Australian commercial bush food crop after macadamia, quandong and bush tomato. Plants that fruit well have been selected, improved and cloned to grow thousands of plants. After harvesting, Muntrie berries are made into jam, sauce, chutney and other tasty foods.

DANIELLE QUARMBY/OUTBACK PRIDE

Kurrajongs
— bottle trees

Family: Sterculiaceae
Genus: Brachychiton

Australia has 30 of the world's 31 Brachychiton *species. Many schools, parks, farm driveways and fence lines have ornamental plantings of Australia's best known kurrajong,* Brachychiton populneus, *an evergreen which grows naturally in open forests of eastern Australia. The most famous living kurrajong, at Mt Annan in New South Wales, is over 500 years old. It is protected and listed as a heritage tree, sacred to the Dharawal people who call it "Dooligah" — giant hairy man — and tell their children a legend associated with it.*

Above: Red-flowering Kurrajong flower in bud.

FLORAL EMBLEM

Darwin's floral emblem is a deciduous kurrajong, *Brachychiton paradoxus*. It grows throughout Northern Territory woodlands, producing striking red bell flowers on bare branches in the dry season.

IAN MORRIS

BOTTLE TREES

During 1845, on his journey from Sydney to the Gulf of Carpentaria, explorer Thomas Mitchell couldn't believe his eyes when he came across the strangest tree he'd ever seen — a kurrajong or Queensland Bottle Tree (*Brachychiton rupestris*).

Aborigines knew they could find water by boring through the tree's bark.

the FACTS!

EVIDENCE OF LONG ANCESTRY in kurrajongs was found in New South Wales in the form of a 50-million-year-old fossilised leaf.

THE NOW RARE Desert Kurrajong (*Brachychiton gregorii*) of Central Australian sandplains has been a valued water and food source for thousands of years for Pitjantjatjara and Arrernte people. Crows feast on the ripe seeds which come out in their droppings, then are collected, cleaned and eaten by local people.

ABORIGINAL PEOPLE make string from the inner bark of kurrajongs to weave dilly bags, baskets and fishing nets.

NUTTY SEEDS of *Brachychiton populneus* have a high nutrition value with 18% protein and 25% fat and can be eaten raw, roasted or ground into flour for damper making.

EXPLORERS such as Ludwig Leichhardt and early settlers collected kurrajong pods (below) which they husked, roasted and ground the seeds for use in coffee.

GREG HARM/SPP

Lechenaultias
— sensitive flowers

Family: Goodeniaceae
Genus: Lechenaultia

Blue Lechenaultia (Lechenaultia biloba) is the best known species in this genus, with its mass of superb blue flowers. People love this memorable flowering plant so much that it has become a garden favourite, mostly because it's so blue, but also because of its prostrate spreading nature. It is easily grown from cuttings. During early spring in Western Australia, it "paints" the heaths with patches of blue as far north as Eneabba and south to the jarrah forests near Manjimup.

Above, top to bottom: Yellow Lechenaultia (*Lechenaultia linarioides*); Blue Lechenaultia (*Lechenaultia biloba*).

NATURE'S WREATH

Coming across this curiously shaped plant growing north of Perth (between the towns of Wubin and Mullewa), you'd be forgiven for thinking it was a freshly laid wreath. Each year this perennial plant grows new central green foliage, which in spring is surrounded by a circle of reddish-lemon flowers with winged petals. Plants vary in size from 30–50 cm diameter.

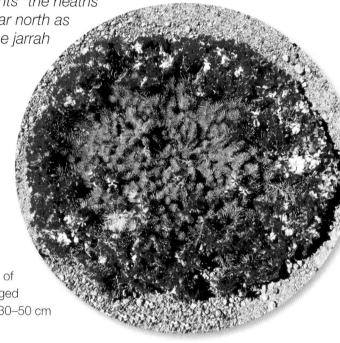

KEN STEPNELL/SPP

the FACTS!

AUSTRALIA HAS TWENTY SPECIES within the *Lechenaultia* genus, seventeen endemic to Western Australia and three in central Australia and the Northern Territory.

SEEDS OF *LECHENAULTIA* are known to remain dormant until they experience a bushfire, when germination is caused by chemicals in the smoke.

THE SOUTHERN ARRERNTE people of central Australia have several uses for Tangled Lechenaultia (*Lechenaultia divaricata*). Fleshy young roots were dug up for food and a strong, hard-setting glue came from more mature roots of the plants.

LIPSTICK-RED FLOWERS

In late spring, low-growing Red Lechenaultia (*Lechenaultia formosa*, below and left), surprises passers-by with stunning displays of bright red flowers growing in the Albany and Ravensthorpe regions of Western Australia.

Lichen
— a working alliance

Lichen depends on a cooperative association between two different living organisms, a fungus and a tiny microscopic alga. The alga lives in the fungus's mycelium, using light energy to carry out photosynthesis and so produce food for the fungus.

AN IMPORTANT ROLE for the fungus is to absorb mineral nutrients, so that is the reason lichens are often seen on terracotta tiles, timber, pavements and rocks.

Lichens live in temperate and tropical climates and in many habitats from alpine to coastal. Some coastal areas have massive boulders covered by large patches of brick-orange, golden-yellow or black lichen. Coastal lichens are amazing survivors, which tolerate being constantly splashed by cold waves and buffeted by salt-laden winds. One main result of their rock-dwelling habit is a speeding-up of the weathering of rocks.

Above: A tree-dwelling, lichen-coloured Leaf-tailed Gecko blends very well with lichen on the tree.

LICHEN MOTHS

Can you imagine eating lichen? Australia has 215 Lichen Moths, and lichen is the food of the larval moths (caterpillars). Caterpillars love it! Lichen has some very toxic chemicals which the caterpillars ingest — ready to use as a defence mechanism against predators. If you live in Sydney you may have seen tiny, tufted caterpillars on the tiles and woodwork of older buildings. These are the larvae of the Banded Lichen Moth (*Eutane terminalis*).

Below: For geologists, identification of rocks is not straightforward when lichen gives them a totally different colour.

the FACTS!

OVER ONE MILLION SPECIES of lichen are estimated to exist in the world.

AUSTRALIA HAS 473 GENERA with 3345 described species. Queensland has the most lichen, with 1664 species, and 286 of these are endemic.

SCIENTISTS MAY ASSIST medical science in the future by finding ways to use some of the unusual chemicals produced by lichens.

LITMUS PAPER is made using soluble blue dye obtained from lichen. When litmus paper is used to test solutions, the paper turns red if acid is present.

LICHENS ARE INDICATORS of air quality, so can be used to monitor change. Lichens avoid places with a high level of air pollution and are especially sensitive to sulphur dioxide. A city with lots of lichen indicates that the environment is relatively free of pollution.

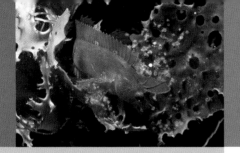

Above: Bull kelp and fish amongst kelp.

Marine Plants
— all at sea

The world's oceans, where life began, have more than 25,000 species of seaweed. There are 1300 described species in Australia, but it is estimated that over 2000 species exist. Seaweeds belong to the Kingdom Protista. Plants living in the sea need sunlight to carry out photosynthesis, so live as close to the surface of the sea as they can. The bubbles they release as a waste product are oxygen. Seaweeds are not found any deeper than 30 m.

the FACTS!

A GLASSFUL OF SEAWATER contains hundreds of different types of microscopic single-celled phytoplankton. "Phyto" is from Greek and means "plant".

NEARLY HALF of Earth's oxygen is produced by ocean-living phytoplankton.

EARTH'S TEMPERATURE is cooler when plenty of phytoplankton are using up carbon dioxide.

NEAR THE SEA'S SURFACE is where phytoplankton need to be to harvest sunlight for photosynthesis. Plankton protect themselves from harmful ultraviolet rays by manufacturing their own sunscreen.

PHYTOPLANKTON THRIVE when plenty of recycling nutrients (from dead, decomposing sealife) rise to the surface from the bottom of the sea. Where this happens, the vast numbers of phytoplankton make the sea look green.

THE PETROL WE USE for cars, houses and factories comes from crude oil, which has been forming over millions of years in sediment at the ocean floor. When phytoplankton die, their millions of tiny bodies break down to form oil.

ZOOPLANKTON (tiny single-celled animals) eat phytoplankton. So do shellfish, corals, sponges and sea jellies. Phytoplankton are perfect "baby food" for young fish.

Right: "Bull Kelp" is the name given to living species in several genera, but all live along wild-weather coasts.

SEAWEEDS

Seaweeds are the larger marine algae, so are plants without flowers, adapted to turbulent seas. Many attach themselves to rocks with strong holdfasts and their fronds have built-in flotation bladders.

Bright green "Chlorophyta" are found in the intertidal zone, in places like rockpools that are underwater during high tide but exposed during low tide. Tropical areas have the most green seaweed.

Brown algae "Phaeophyta" and red algae "Rhodophyta", growing in deeper water, create the ocean's forests which provide shelter, food and oxygen for many sea creatures. Bull Kelp is a massive brown alga, growing up to five metres tall, with long, leather-like straps. Tasmania's King Island has a Bull Kelp (*Durvillaea potatorum*) industry supplying 5% of the world's requirements of alginates. This substance is extracted from dried kelp for many uses, including the thickening of milkshakes, ice-cream, and fruit juices.

Above: Seals and kelp need similar habitat.

HEALING POWERS

About twenty years ago the seaweed, Wakame (*Undaria pinnatifida*) appeared in Australia's coastal waters and has since been declared a marine pest. It is thought to have arrived in the ballast of a Northern Hemisphere ship collecting wood chip. A company on the east coast of Tasmania is harvesting this brown alga, and processing it to extract potent anti-virals called fucoidans which help sufferers of HIV, Herpes Simplex and Influenza A and B.

Above: Seahorse in a seagrass "meadow".

Below, top and bottom: Dugongs are "the cows of the sea", grazing tropical seagrasses. An adult can eat up to 28 kg per day; A mangrove tree's snorkel-like roots rise from the mud, obtaining oxygen for the tree in a waterlogged environment.

SEAGRASS

Seagrass is not a real "grass", but is a very special flowering plant — in fact the only representative of the angiosperms that lives in seawater. Seagrass used to be a land plant about 100 million years ago. Now there are 58 sea-living species, with over 30 in Australian coastal waters. Australia's west coast, with 27 species, is the site of one of the world's largest seagrass areas. Seagrass needs sunlight to thrive. Pollution from shipping, dredging and mining activities, run-off of agricultural and industrial waste and human sewage all cause sediment build-up which can reduce the light seagrass needs and cause it to die.

Above: Mangrove stems and roots, widely spaced or intricately tangled, provide vital shelter for young fish to improve their chances of surviving to adulthood.

SEAGRASS MEADOWS, found right around Australia's coastline, provide a protected habitat for seahorses, seadragons, juvenile fish, crayfish larvae, prawns, turtles and dugongs. There are human uses for seagrass too. Dried, woven seagrass makes excellent mats for use in sand dune rehabilitation programs. At Kingston, in South Australia, dried seagrass *Posidonia australis* is harvested from beaches to make liquid plant fertiliser.

the FACTS!

FORESTS OF MANGROVES cover 11,600 sq km of Australia, protecting and stabilising parts of the coastline by absorbing the energy from stormy winds and waves, and holding mud and sand in place. Australia has about 35 of the world's 65 mangrove species. Only two are considered endemic.

FISH DEPEND ON MANGROVES. They use these nurturing habitats as nurseries for their young. Many shrimps, crabs, worms, shellfish, and insects are also protected from strong tidal movement.

MANGROVES EXCLUDE SALT, using their roots to filter out up to 90% of it. If the salt level is still too high, leaves can quickly excrete salt or stems can send it to an old leaf, which will drop off.

SEEDLINGS GROW SHOOTS and roots while still attached to the parent tree. They drop off into the sea with the advantage that they are ready to start growing the moment they find a calm, soft-bottomed place to take root.

Mosses
— nature's water storage

Above: Moss-covered boulders in Rainforest Creek at Mount Lewis, North Queensland.

the FACTS!

TASMANIA'S RAINFORESTS hold at least 80 moss species. Globally, it is estimated that there are 9500–15,000 species of moss belonging to many families.

SOME MOSSES ARE EPIPHYTIC, growing on other live plants for support.

AFTER SEVERE DROUGHT, moss makes a surprising recovery. Having looked dead, it can come to life again quickly after rain.

DRY SPHAGNUM MOSS has incredible water-holding capacity. The Inuit of Alaska collected it from the tundras, dried and used it on their babies for disposable nappies.

MODERN USES for Dry Sphagnum Moss are many, and include propagation, potting for medium and lining for hanging baskets.

Mosses belong to the Bryophyta division of the Plant Kingdom. The closely related Liverworts and Hornworts used to be included in this division, but have since been separated. Mosses thrive in damp habitats, carpeting forest floors, clinging to living plants, fallen logs and boulders in rivers. These soft, miniature plants provide a vital rainforest role in regulating evaporation, erosion and run off.

MOSSES DO NOT have a vascular system like most other plants and cannot transport liquids and nutrients up inside their stems. Instead, mosses have the ability to draw water up from outside; they soak up moisture just like a sponge. Their water-collecting role is extremely important for the health of the rainforest. Mosses slowly release moisture, helping to monitor and regulate humidity during dry periods. Spiders, worms, snails, insects and other tiny forest fauna find shelter and protection amongst the moss. Ferns and other plants find moss an ideal medium from which to regenerate.

Above: Sphagnum Moss makes an excellent groundcover in which other plants can find a toehold. *Below:* The forest floor provides ideal conditions for mosses to flourish. They completely shroud this fallen trunk.

SPHAGNUM MOSS HABITATS
— MANY USES

Corroboree Frogs (right) depend on Sphagnum Moss (*Sphagnum cymbifolioides*), tunnelling into it for their homes and to mate and lay eggs in the moist water-holding mass. It's estimated that Australia has only 300 of these very endangered, boldly marked, frogs living in mossy bogs, high (above 1300 m) in alpine areas.

IAN MORRIS

Mulla mullas
— mulla mulla colour

Family: Amaranthaceae
Genus: Ptilotus

Fluffy mulla mulla flowers come in a range of soft colours, including white, cream, lemon, pale green, silver, grey, pink, mauve and red. The genus name — Ptilotus — means "feathered", and flower shapes range from foxtails to pussy tails, feather dusters, hairy longtails and pom-poms. Every fluffy flower has five thin hairy petals.

Above: Mulla mullas on a red sand-dune with Uluru on the horizon.

MULLA MULLAS ARE mainly ephemeral plants of arid areas, "making their mark" by flowering profusely after soaking rains. Some mulla mullas are hardy perennial herbs with a deep root system. Tangled Mulla Mulla (*Ptilotus latifolius*), is an annual of sand dunes in the red centre and looks like a tangled mass of silvery white "cotton balls".

Above: The soft fluffy plants of Silvertails (*Ptilotus obovatus*), found throughout mainland Australia, were used to line baby-carrying wooden coolamins in Central Australia where it is a very common plant. Aborigines knew they could dig up edible grubs amongst the roots of this plant.

MULLA MULLA
SYMBOL

Warlpiri people of Central Australia say that mulla mulla — especially Tall Mulla Mulla (*P. exultatus*) — is a male sex symbol.

Right: Tall Mulla Mulla.

the FACTS!

AUSTRALIA DOMINATES the mulla mulla world, with its 100 endemic species. Only one species is from elsewhere — Malaysia.

AN EXTRACT from mulla mulla plants is being used in the treatment of skin cancers.

TALL MULLA MULLA (*Ptilotus exaltatus*) can be an amazing pot plant and makes a great show in gardens too. In Germany it won awards for being the "Potted Flowering Plant of the Year" for both 1991 and 1993.

MULLA MULLA FLOWERS are becoming more and more sought-after for the floral industry. In NSW a licence is necessary for picking from the wild or growing Tall Mulla Mulla (*Ptilotus exaltatus*) and Silvertails (*Ptilotus obovatus*).

"SMOKEBUSH" or "Cottonbush" are other names given to Silvertail (*Ptilotus obovatus)* by florists.

WHEN NEXT IN CANBERRA, visit the Australian National Botanic Gardens to see *Ptilotus drummondii* growing in the rockery.

PTILOTUS MANGLESII, a pink and white mulla mulla native to Western Australia, is grown from root cuttings at the Wisley Royal Horticultural Society Garden in England.

Orchids
— a very big family

Family: Orchidaceae

Worldwide, Orchidaceae — a contender with Asteraceae for the title of largest flowering plant family — has 800 genera, and up to 35,000 species. Australia has over 100 genera and up to 1400 native orchids. 80% of Australia's orchids are endemic.

Above: Zebra Orchid (*Caladenia cairnsiana)* has a heavily striped lip, very much like the markings on a zebra. It grows in coastal areas and woodland in south-west Western Australia from Gin Gin to east of Esperance and flowers from August to November.

Right: Lazy Spider Orchid (*Caladenia multiclavia).*

the FACTS!

LAZY SPIDER ORCHID (*Caladenia multiclavia),* grows on the ground and flowers during September to October from Ravensthorpe to the Wongan Hills area. This striped orchid looks like a spider lying on its back with its legs in the air.

LIVING UNDERGROUND is a way of life for two Australian orchids belonging to the genus *Rhizanthella.* They never see the light of day.

OVER 150 ORCHID SOCIETIES exist in Australia. People show enormous interest in these amazing flowers.

ALL 70 AUSTRALIAN SPECIES of *Dendrobium* orchids are under cultivation. New Zealand has only one native species of *Dendrobium.*

TWO THIRDS OF AUSTRALIA'S orchids are terrestrial, which means they live on the ground (rather than on trees or rocks). Most are deciduous; dormant during hot summers, and sprouting in autumn.

TO SEE ORCHID SEED, the smallest seed of all plants, you almost need a microscope — 1.25 million seeds make up one gram.

SUN ORCHIDS

These deciduous, mainly temperate, terrestrial orchids depend on a sunny day, and open their petals for a few hours around noon. The world has 50 species, with 37 endemic to Australia and the rest native to New Zealand, the Philippines, Java, Timor and New Caledonia. Some Sun Orchids in New Zealand are the same species as in Australia and it is thought that seed has been carried across the Tasman Sea by wind to become established in New Zealand. Many Sun Orchids are blue, a very rare colour for orchids. Scented Sun Orchid (*Thelymitra aristata)* flowers in an intense blue from September to January in heathlands of New South Wales, Victoria and South Australia.

A BURST OF SUNSHINE IN FLOWER

Cowslip Orchid (*Caladenia flava)* has a widespread distribution in Western Australia from Murchison River (above Geraldton on the west coast), to Israelite Bay (east of Esperance, on the south coast). This stunning orchid in sunshine-yellow speckled with red, flowers between July and December.

Above, top and bottom: Cowslip Orchid; The large flowers of Swamp Orchid (*Phaius tancarvilliae).*

Left: Scented Sun Orchid.

Conservation Watch

Many Australian orchids have a Vulnerable or Endangered status. 70 of 100 Australian species of *Caladenia* are Rare or Threatened. Fortunately the Australian National Botanic Gardens in Canberra have many species of *Caladenia* in cultivation.

FLORAL EMBLEM

One third of Australia's orchids are epiphytic, growing on branches, tree trunks and in the cracks and crevices of rocks. Cooktown Orchid (*Dendrobium phalaenopsis*) is an epiphytic orchid, growing in tropical areas of high summer rainfall in northern Queensland and also in the Torres Strait Islands. It is also Queensland's floral emblem. In some locations, this plant has become endangered. The common name comes from Cooktown, a coastal town north of Cairns, named by Captain James Cook. Cooktown Orchids were taken to England in 1852 to be investigated and named by botanists. These much admired Australian orchids are grown in humid glasshouses in England.

the FACTS!

DECEPTION is the way that an estimated one third of the world's orchid species are pollinated. Brightly coloured and sweetly perfumed orchids advertise cunningly, luring insects to visit their flowers, and tricking them into thinking they can gather nectar.

DONKEY ORCHIDS (below), widespread in southern Australia, are found in every State of Australia. These 37 species have two erect petals characteristically shaped like donkey ears. They mimic Peaflowers to trick insects into visiting them for pollen transfer. Sandplain Donkey Orchid (*Diuris corymbosa*), found from Albany to Dongara in Western Australia, flowers during September and October.

ORCHID TRICKERY

About 100 species of Australian terrestrial orchids from nine genera have an incredible method of deception. A pheromone, that humans can't smell, is released by the orchid and this matches the exact chemical pheromone used by a female insect to entice a mate. Once attracted to the flower by the pheromone, the male insect tries to mate with part of the flower that visually looks like a female insect of his kind. This sexual practice is called pseudocopulation. The male bull-dog ant tries to mate with the Hare Orchid (*Leptoceras menziesii*), which releases a pheromone matching the female bull-dog ant. Western Australia's Common Dragon Orchid (*Drakonorchis barbarossa*), mimics a wingless female wasp inviting male wasps for pseudocopulation.

Below, left to right: Common Dragon Orchid (*Drakonorchis barbarossa*); Curled-tongue Shell Orchid (*Pterostylis rogersii*).

Paperbarks
— getting their feet wet

Above: A large proportion of *Melaleuca* tree volume is made up of its layered, papery bark.

Right: Paperbark trees grow together in stands where conditions are right.

the FACTS!

PAPERBARK, on the trunks of quite a few melaleucas, is papery thin layers of cork, which can be easily peeled off with little damage to the tree.

A PAPERBARK WRAP provides sunscreen and insulation for the tree's trunk.

TO KEEP ABORIGINAL BABIES warm, mothers wrapped them in soft sheets of paperbark. Disposable nappies were made from paperbark too.

A HEAP of soft paperbark makes a comfortable bush mattress.

THE PLIABLE, waterproof and antiseptic qualities of soft paperbark made it an excellent bandage for wounds in traditional Aboriginal life.

SPLINTS to support broken limbs were also made by Aboriginal people. They wrapped the limbs in sheets of strong paperbark.

LARGE DURABLE SHEETS of paperbark were used by Aborigines to provide a waterproof roof for their shelter.

Family: Myrtaceae
Genus: Melaleuca

Australia has the world's majority of Melaleuca *spp., with 176 named species, but it's likely there are up to 200. Western Australia has at least 100 species.* Melaleuca *species with bottlebrush-shaped flowers, are often confused with the* Callistemon *genus. One of the main differences is that melaleuca blooms always have their stamens in bundles of five and callistemons have separated stamens. Melaleucas feature soft fluffy flowers that come in every colour of the rainbow except blue, and their nectar is a great attraction for birds and bees.*

CURE-ALL OIL

Antiseptic oil with incredible healing power is distilled from the foliage of *Melaleuca alternifolia* and marketed nationally and internationally for its anti-microbial properties. This germicidal oil contains "terpinen-4-ol" which penetrates the skin and is helpful in clearing up wounds, pimples, boils, warts, cold sores, fungal and bacterial skin infections and more. Tea-tree oil is also added to some soap, antiseptic cream, shampoo, disinfectant and insect repellent.

PAPERBARKS THRIVE IN SWAMPS

right across northern Australia and are used to a very damp life during the wet season. Some paperbarks growing in swamps and beside rivers are known to be able to live for hundreds of years. One of their secrets for a long life is to develop a pocket of air inside their trunks, allowing them to breathe when they become submerged in water for months at a time.

TEA-TREE OIL is distilled from trees harvested from plantations in NSW and Qld, and during 1994 commercial production was 130 tonnes, worth $7 million to Australia.

Left and right: Magpie Geese (*Anseranas semipalmata*) congregate in large flocks in wet grasslands and paperbark swamps. They feed on aquatic vegetation.

Conservation Watch

Compared with other forests in Australia, melaleuca forests and woodlands have not suffered to the same extent. But threats exist, and these include drainage of swamp habitats and building of floodgates.

MELALEUCA MIGRATION

A long time ago, Narrow-leaved Paperbark (*Melaleuca linariifolia*) was taken to England, where it has become a widely cultivated garden plant. It is called "Snow in Summer", due to the mass of fluffy, cloud-like "bottlebrush" flowers it has in summer. Birds come for the insects, which are frequent visitors during flowering. It is native to bush locations in Qld and NSW and grows to a height of about 10 m.

Left: Narrow-leaved Paperbark.

Above: This paperbark tree provides a perfect place for this colony of Spectacled Flying-foxes to hang out.

MEDICINE CHEST TREES

The leaves of several melaleucas are suitable for medicinal use and have been used as a medicine chest for thousands of years by Aborigines.

Melaleuca symphyocarpa provided much medical assistance to people on Groote Eylandt. Scrunched-up leaves released a vapour which could be inhaled to ease the congestion of colds. A headache was treated by rubbing leaves onto the forehead, releasing a strong medicinal aroma. Liniment was made from leaves to rub on the body to relieve the pain of aches and sprains.

Above: The leaves of Thyme Honey Myrtle (*Melaleuca thymifolia*) actually smell like thyme.

Left: In some areas, paperbark roots interwine to form buttress-like mounds.

the FACTS!

INDIGENOUS people rolled paperbark for torches and fires.

THE WATERPROOF NATURE of paperbark made it a perfect material for Aborigines to patch canoe holes.

FOOD WRAPS were made from paperbark bark. Meat, fish and vegetables wrapped in bark could be cooked on hot coals.

WHEN GROOTE EYLANDT people cook cockles on hot coals, they add flavour to them with leaves of *Melaleuca acacioides*.

IRLPERLE is the name given by Arrernte people of Central Australia to local paperbarks. They use them to trap fish, by blocking the stream with a bushy barrier of branches.

KATH WALKER, well-known Australian poet of the Noonuccal people from Stradbroke Island, has an Aboriginal name, "Oodgeroo" — which is the name for White Paperbark (*Melaleuca leucadendra*).

Palms, Pandanus & Cycads
— striking silhouettes

PALMS

Australia has about 60 of the world's 2800 species of palms, with at least 50% found in the rainforests. There are many different genera of palms. North Queensland is rich in palm species. Darwin and Brisbane Botanical Gardens have large palm collections, and Townsville has a "Palmetum".

Right: Fan Palms (*Licuala ramsayi*) in Daintree National Park. With leaves that radiate out into fan-shaped circles, they look like parasols when viewed from below. *Below:* Foxtail palm.

the FACTS!

TWENTY *LIVISTONA* SPECIES (in the Arecaceae family) live in Australia. Leaves of *Livistona humilis*, from north Queensland, are used extensively for weaving baskets.

PALMS ARE "MONOCOT" flowering plants belonging to the Arecaceae family. The embryos of these plants have one seed leaf — monocotyledon.

CASSOWARIES, flying-foxes, possums, mammals and birds eat the fleshy fruits from palms.

DATE PALMS were introduced to central Australia by Afghan cameleers, during the 19th Century. A date farm was established in Alice Springs by relocating many old date palms from outlying stations.

OTHER FOODS from palm trees include sago, bananas and coconuts.

COCONUT PALMS are not endemic to Australia. They are seen on the fringes of tropical Australian beaches because coconuts have floated across the oceans from other countries. Every part of a coconut palm has uses for humans. It is said that if you plant a coconut palm when a baby is born, the palm will provide coconuts for the life of the baby.

WODYETI'S LEGACY

Foxtail Palm (*Wodyetia bifurcata*) has a frond just like the bushy tail on a fox. Its botanical name honours Aboriginal bushman, Wodyeti, who died in 1978. He was custodian to traditional knowledge about this outstanding Australian palm and its remote whereabouts. Foxtail Palms grow naturally on gravel hilltops at Bathurst Bay and at Cape Melville on the Cape York Peninsula.

RARE ANCIENT PALM

Red Cabbage Palm (*Livistona mariae*) is a remnant rainforest plant which has survived for millions of years, originating from the time when most of Australia was covered by rainforests. In Palm Valley, Central Australia, these amazing palms — some 300 years old — probably owe their survival to a constant supply of water which seeps down the sides of the gorge and also comes from springs.

PALM LOOK-A-LIKES

Though they look very much like palms, plants of the genus *Pandanus* are not palms. Birds use the ragged, strap-like leaves as a haven for hiding, shelter and nest-building. Coastal Pandanus are common beside the sea in tropical Australia, providing windbreaks and erosion stability.

WATER PANDANUS

Yellow Waters Billabong in Kakadu features many Water Pandanus (*Pandanus aquaticus*), which create important habitats used by a range of wildlife. Arafura File Snakes live underneath the roots, Rufous Night Herons roost in the branches and Crimson Finches nest amongst the strappy leaves. Azure Kingfishers watch for insects, Rainbow Bee-eaters flit around in search of insects, and Pig-nosed Turtles devour Pandanus fruit as it falls into the water.

CYCADS

The world has about 160 species of cycad, belonging to ten genera. Australia has 26 species belonging to the genus *Cycas* and twelve species of the *Macrozamia* genus. Cycads belong to the plant group Gymnospermae. They are non-flowering plants with seed-bearing cones. The Daintree Rainforest has 21% of Australia's cycad species.

Left, above and below: Pandanus growing on sand at Fraser Island, Qld; The cycad *Macrozamia macdonnellii* at Trephina Gorge Nature Park, in the East MacDonnell Ranges.

the FACTS!

CYCAD SEEDS poisoned some of Captain James Cook's sailors when they ate them at the Endeavour River near Cooktown in Queensland in 1770. The river was named after Cook's ship, *Endeavour*.

ABORIGINAL WOMEN know to leech out the poison from seeds of some cycad species by soaking them in running water. This makes them edible. In northern Australia seeds of the toxic *Cycas armstrongii* were turned into flour and regarded as good "walkabout tucker".

CYCAD LEAF TOXICITY can cause spinal cord damage in cattle.

CYCADS ARE HOST PLANTS for the butterfly Cycad Blue (*Theclinesthes onycha*). Only young tender fronds are larval food.

EUROS AND WALLABIES eat the thick seed covers from the rare MacDonnell Ranges Cycad (*Macrozamia macdonnellii*), which grows in gorges and on rocky hillsides in Central Australia.

DINOSAUR FOOD

Australia's cycads are closely related to the cycads of the Jurassic Period, when dinosaurs roamed the Earth. Plant-eating dinosaurs must have had "cast iron" stomachs to be able to digest cycads! Fossilised Australian plant-eating dinosaurs, called Sauropods, have been found with round, worn, stones beside them. These "gastroliths" (stomach stones) were eaten on purpose, enabling them to grind down tough vegetation like cycads.

Pea Flowers
— lovely legumes

Family: Fabaceae

The pea flower family is huge, with 500 genera and 12,000 species in the world. In Australia there are 140 genera and 1100 species. Pea flowers are shaped like colourful little butterflies, each flower having five petals of different shapes. The back petal is large and erect, then there are two wing-shaped petals at the sides, and a further two petals fused to make the keel, which holds ten stamens. The ovary of the flower changes into a pod to provide protection for the fertilised peas. These plants are legumes with nodules on their roots, which have the ability to take nitrogen from the atmosphere with the help of tiny bacteria in the soil.

Above: Smooth Darling Pea (*Swainsona galegifolia*).

the FACTS!

TAMMAR WALLABIES on Kangaroo Island, South Australia dig up and eat the roots of Coast Swainson-pea (*Swainsona lessertiifolia*).

WILDLIFE BROWSE on many pea flower plants and livestock on some.

GLOBALLY, PEA FLOWERS are important providers of food for humans. All the beans and peas we eat come from this same family.

ANTS HELP the pea flower reproductive process by collecting and "planting" seeds. Ants eat the fleshy appendages on the seeds then leave them safely stored underground, ready to grow.

PEA FLOWERS ARE "PIONEERS" after bushfires — they can quickly recolonise an area.

FLAME PEAS

Chorizema is an endemic genus of 25 species; 24 in the south-west of Western Australia and one species found in Queensland and New South Wales.

Nature has put together a stunning combination of pink and orange in these flowers. Heart-leaved Flame Pea (Chorizema cordatum) sometimes with a climbing habit, has brilliant coral and orange flowers — found in heath and woodlands of south-west WA.

Above: Heart-leaved Flame Pea (*Chorizema cordatum*).

BIRDFLOWERS

The genus *Crotalaria* has 26 species in Australia. These plants with sausage-shaped pods rattle when they are dry. Some of the Birdflower species are known to cause livestock poisoning, due to their foliage containing pyrrolizidine alkaloid, which can damage the liver.

Striking Green Birdflower (*Crotalaria cunninghamii*), grows in sandy places such as coastal dunes and river beds in arid areas of WA, NT, Qld and NSW. This endangered plant has a widespread distribution including the Kimberley Ranges.

Left: Green Birdflower (*Crotalaria cunninghamii*).

Far left: Wild Sarsaparilla (*Hardenbergia comptoniana*).

FLORAL EMBLEM

Sturt's Desert Pea (*Swainsona formosa*) covers wide
patches of desert with red and is South Australia's floral
emblem. It flourishes after heavy rain, surprising travellers in
Central Australia who have the pleasure of seeing it along
road edges where it thrives due to the run-off from extra rain.
William Dampier discovered these striking flowers and wrote of seeing
them on Rosemary Island, Western Australia, during his second
voyage to Australia in 1699 on HMS *Roebuck*. The specimens he
collected are held in the Oxford University herbarium in England.

HAPPY WANDERINGS

Only three species of *Hardenbergia* exist in
Australia. False Sarsparilla (*Hardenbergia
violacea*) is often sold in plant nurseries
as the "Happy Wanderer" — because
the plant has a habit of spreading in all
directions, making an excellent ground
cover. It grows naturally in heavy clay soils
in Queensland, New South Wales, Victoria
and Tasmania.

Right: Black Coral Pea (*Kennedia nigricans*)
of Western Australia has flowers of black and
gold, which is a very rare colour combination.
This plant is a rampant creeper with prolific
growth, especially following a bushfire.

Below: False Sarsparilla.

the FACTS!

STURT'S DESERT PEA SEED is
commercially available.

BETTER GERMINATION OF
Sturt's Desert Pea results if seeds
are soaked overnight in a cup of
boiling water.

NORTH-FACING LOCATIONS with
plenty of sun are best for seeds of
Sturt's Desert Pea. They thrive in
hot, dry conditions.

HORTICULTURALISTS sometimes
graft Sturt's Desert Pea onto rootstock of New Zealand's Kaka Beak
(*Clianthus puniceus*), to improve the
plant's ability to grow in cold and
humid climates.

DURING GOLDRUSH DAYS,
gold seekers searched for False
Sarsparilla growing in the goldfields,
as these plants were said to signal
the places to dig for gold.

Above: Hoop Pine (*Araucaria cunninghamii*).

"Pines"
— plants with "naked seeds"

Division: Coniferophyta

"Pines" or conifers as they are correctly referred to in the southern hemisphere are part of the group of plants that has "naked seeds". They hold their seeds in cones instead of in fruits and they don't have flowers. Conifers date back to the Triassic Period (250–205 million years ago) when they were the most abundant plants on Pangaea. From fossils, we know about ancestors of Australian conifers, and that huge plant-eating dinosaurs used to graze on these tasty trees.

the FACTS!

"WINGS" OR "BLADDERS" have evolved on the pollen of some species, to help it fly with the wind.

WIND HAS BEEN KNOWN to carry pollen up to 6000 m high and as far as 5000 km away.

THE EARLIEST POLLEN FOUND dates back to 135 million years ago and comes from the southern conifer family: Podocarpaceae.

SCIENTISTS HAVE DISCOVERED that fossil pollen can tell us what life was like on Earth long ago. Pollen with a mutation shows that there was a stressful time on Earth, such as damage to the ozone layer or massive atmospheric change.

MOST CONIFERS ARE EVERGREEN with needle or scale-like leaves and cones. Each tree has both male and female structures, and the trees depend on wind for pollination.

FAMOUS HUON PINE

Huon Pine (*Lagarostrobos franklinii*) is the world's only member of the genus *Lagarostrobos*. Huon Pine fossils, dated at 10–20 million years old, were discovered in a coal deposit at Yallourn in Victoria. Tasmania has 10,500 ha of remnant Huon Pine vegetation, with most protected in a World Heritage Site. There is an amazing stand of Huon Pines at Mt Read, originating from a single tree, and dating back 10,500 years to the last glacier. All living trees in this stand are genetically identical; all are male and they cover an area of one hectare on a hillside of Mt Read, which is in a subalpine area of Tasmania. How do we know this veteran stand originated so long ago? Sediment cores from Lake Johnson indicate matching Huon Pine pollen, 10,500 years old, from the original tree. Over thousands of years, the tree cloned itself. As snow forced branches into the soil, roots formed and it gradually spread out, creating a massive stand.

NATIVE "PINES"

There are about twenty *Callitris* species in the world with only two outside Australia, in New Caledonia.

Murray River Aboriginal people made 4 m long fish spears from Murray Pine (*Callitris pressii*), they called "Maroong". These were also used as canoe poles.

Murray Pines were very important to Europeans coming to Australia, providing termite-resistant timber for building.

Left: Huon Pine (*Lagarostrobos franklinii*) growing in the Tahune Forest, south-east Tasmania.

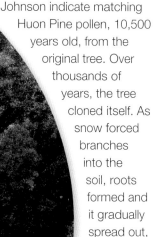

Conservation Watch

Mt Annan Botanic Gardens in NSW holds a clone of each Wollemi Pine from the wild and has propagated over 500 trees. A forestry nursery in Queensland has been licensed to cultivate Wollemi Pines to be sold in nurseries and overseas.

Above: Queensland Kauri, (*Agathis robusta*), thrives at Fraser Island, growing alongside Hoop Pine and dominating the rainforest canopy. Unfortunately most of this kauri in other areas has been felled as softwood timber for plywood and furniture. New Zealand Kauri (*Agathis australis*), with 2000-year-old living specimens, is closely related to Australia's trees.

Below: The female cone of a Norfolk pine.

BUNYA PINE

Bunya Pines (*Araucaria bidwilli*) can grow to 40 m high and produce heavy, pineapple-shaped cones, weighing up to 10 kg. The cones are full of edible 5 cm nuts and these are sometimes available for purchase in markets. Bunya Pines tend to have bumper crops every three years, and to coincide with this huge harvest opportunity, bunya feasts were traditionally celebrated by over 700 Aboriginal people of the Blackall Ranges. Bunya is a Bundjalung Aboriginal name from Northern NSW.

the FACTS!

NORFOLK PINE (*Araucaria heterophylla*) is endemic to Norfolk Island. Norfolk Pines were logged and sent by sea from Norfolk Island to assist the building process of the First Settlement at Port Jackson. Hawaii has large plantations of Norfolk Pine for timber production.

ARAUCARIACEAE, the primitive conifer family, gets its name from the Araucani, an Indigenous group of people from South America.

SEDIMENT CORE CONTENTS taken from Queensland's Eromanga Basin, have shown scientists that ancestors of the family were there during the mid-Cretaceous Period.

HOOP PINE is the most important native conifer for softwood production in Queensland. It takes 50 years to mature and there are now 42,000 hectares of converted rainforest in plantations managed by Queensland Forest Service.

HOOP PINE (*Araucaria cunninghamii*) is a rainforest conifer with ancestry from millions of years ago. It used to cover more of Australia than it does today.

WOLLEMI PINE — "DINOSAUR TREE"

One day in 1994, a NSW park ranger discovered trees he'd never seen before — and everyone had thought extinct for about the last 200 million years. What a find! He was looking at Wollemi Pine (*Wollemia nobilis*) with a history stretching back to when dinosaurs were about. These are the world's rarest and most endangered ancient trees and fewer than 100 exist in a remote chasm of Wollemi National Park, in the Greater Blue Mountains of New South Wales. As you can imagine, their location is a closely guarded secret. All are single sex trees with fern-like leaves, and chocolate-bubble-like bark, and the tallest is 38 m high.

Right: The distinctive foliage of Wollemi Pine baffled researchers for ages, until they were guided by very similar-looking plant fossils pulled from museum shelves.

Below: Hoop Pine (*Araucaria cunninghamii*).

She-oaks
— mistaken identity

Family: Casuarinaceae
Genera: Allocasuarina and Casuarina

Fossil pollen records tell us that she-oaks have been in Australia for at least 60 million years. Most she-oaks are "dioecious", meaning that individual plants have either male or female flowers — but not both on the same plant. Females have bigger flowers and produce the fantastically textured cones, which will only release the winged seeds if dropped from the tree or burnt. Very dark, tough, thick, cork-like bark provides a protective cover for the trunk, insulating it from abrasive sandy winds, extremely high and low temperatures and water loss. They are well adapted to life on sand dunes. Some species of she-oaks even have aerial roots to cope with life in swampy areas.

Above: She-oaks are typical of sandy and rocky coastal areas, but are also found inland and are quite hardy trees.

Below: She-oak cones release winged seeds.

GREG HARM/SPP

SHELTER FROM THE STORM

Some species of the genus *Casuarina* are grown extensively overseas, to provide shelter, ensure farm sustainability and assist in erosion control. Masses of River She-oak (*Casuarina cunninghamiana*) are planted along canals and for soil-binding in the Sahara desert in Egypt.

Left: When you visit central Australia take time to stand under a Desert Oak (*Allocasuarina decaisneana*) and listen. You'll hear a whispering wind song, as breezes pass through the needle-like foliage.

the FACTS!

RECENT RESEARCH has discovered that She-oaks have haemoglobin in their nitrogen-making nodules, and some in their roots. We have this chemical, as an oxygen carrier, in our blood.

"CASUARINA" comes from the Malay word for Cassowary — and notes the similarity in feather/foliage.

SHE-OAK POLLEN sometimes blows across the Tasman Sea, landing and colouring patches of snow on mountains in New Zealand.

SURVIVAL OF THE FITTEST

Australia's rarest and most endangered cockatoo, the Glossy Black Cockatoo (*Calyptorhynchus lathami*), depends on a regular supply of seeds from the woody cones produced on female She-oak trees. Residents on Kangaroo Island in South Australia are so concerned about the survival of their Glossy Black Cockatoos that they have planted dozens of Drooping She-oak (*Allocasuarina verticillata*) at Reeves Point, Kingscote.

GRAEME CHAPMAN

Tea-trees
— tea & honey

Family: Myrtaceae
Genus: Leptospermum

Australia has 83 of the world's 86 species of Leptospermum. *A few tea-tree species are native to Malaysia, Sumatra, Borneo, Java, Sulawesi, the Philippines and Thailand. Manuka (the Maori name for* Leptospermum scoparium) *is native to both New Zealand and Australia and is being widely researched for its excellent healing powers.*

TEA-TREES ARE ABUNDANT in many wetland habitats and coastal areas of Australia. They provide excellent windbreaks on sand dunes and thrive in poor soils. Silky Tea-tree (*Leptospermum lanigerum*) grows along streams and in swampy places in SA, Vic, Tas and NSW. These trees should not be confused with Melaleuca "tea-tree", known for its oil.

Above: Silky Tea-tree (*Leptospermum lanigerum*) flowers.

Left: Leptospermum macrocarpum, of NSW, has flowers 3 cm in diameter — the largest of all tea-tree species. Five petals surround a striking green centre.

the FACTS!

OLIVE TEA-TREE (*Leptospermum liversidgei*) from wetlands of NSW and Qld, is sold in plant nurseries as a mosquito-repellent plant.

LEMON-SCENTED Tea-tree (*Leptospermum petersonii*) a native of Queensland and New South Wales, is valued for the essential oil Citronella, distilled from leaves and twigs. Oil is used to scent shampoo and other toiletries, as an insect repellent and as a health aid. Kenya and Guatemala grow plantations of this Australian tea-tree to gain oil for medicinal use.

THE OILS from Lemon-Scented Tea-tree are said to have anti-bacterial, anti-fungal and antiseptic qualities against Staphyloccus auereus, Candida albicans and Aspergillas niger.

MANY MELBOURNE-BASED anglers watch for Coastal Tea-tree (*Leptospermum laevigatum*) to begin blooming in September as this sign of nature is said to indicate when snapper enter Port Phillip Bay and it's time to go fishing.

BLUE WRENS, Superb Fairy Wrens, Fantails and Flycatchers like to nest in tea-trees. Grey Fantails leave Tasmania in autumn, fly across Bass Strait and are often seen in Melbourne gardens in March.

MIRACLE HONEY

At the Waikato University Honey Research Centre in New Zealand, in 1981, Dr Peter Molan, Associate Professor in Biochemistry, discovered that honey from Manuka has very high levels of anti-bacterial properties.

Christie Cancer Hospital at Didsbury in Manchester, England, imports Manuka honey from New Zealand to help patients following mouth and throat cancer surgery. Treatment with Manuka honey is believed to reduce the risk of Methicillin Resistant Staphyloccus Aureus (also called "Golden Staph" or "Hospital Superbug"). Manuka honey is also valued for treating leg ulcers on elderly patients.

Left: New South Wales' rare ***Leptospermum spectabile*** from Colo River near Sydney is stunning, with bright red flowers, green centres and white stamens.

Unique Endemic Plants
— exclusive club

Australia has several unique plants belonging to a monotypic genus — meaning there is only one species in the genus. Other Australian plants are known for their unique characteristics.

ALBANY SWAMP DAISY

Albany Swamp Daisy (*Actinodium cunninghamii,* top left) is the only species in the genus globally. It is endemic to Western Australia, growing in sandy places from Fitzgerald River to Albany in the Stirling Range.

POM POM EVERLASTINGS

Australia is the only place in the world where the genus *Cephalipterum* is represented. Pom Pom Everlasting (*Cephalipterum drummondii*, left) is the only species in the genus. Soon after autumn and early winter rains, magical yellow or white balls created by many individual flowers, create stunning carpeting displays beside roads and in bushland in Western Australia.

SOUTHERN CROSS

Xanthosia is an Australian genus of 22 species with at least half belonging to Western Australia. Southern Cross (*Xanthosia rotundifolia*, left) is fairly common in the Stirling Range of Western Australia. Strikingly different flowers resemble the four stars of the constellation of the Southern Cross. These flowers display their beauty by opening on sunny days and closing during the night.

the FACTS!

NATIVE RHODODENDRON, (*R. lochiae*), endemic to Queensland, is one of only two *Rhododendron* species in Australia. Stunning trumpet-shaped red flowers (top right) occur in spring and summer.

FIFTEEN ACTINOTUS SPECIES exist in the world, with fourteen in Australia and one in New Zealand.

FLANNEL FLOWERS (*Actinotus* genus) are insect-pollinated by such insects as flies, wasps and beetles.

SYDNEY FLANNEL FLOWER (*Actinotus helianthi*), which grows in both New South Wales and Queensland, is an admired plant with furry silver foliage, and fantastic daisies with the softest white petals and pale green centres.

FLOWERS HAVE BEEN RAIDED from the wild in the past for the floristry trade. To help stop this practice, Mt Annan Botanic Garden in NSW propagates Flannel Flowers for horticulture by tissue culture.

Waratahs
— beacons of the bush

Family: Proteaceae
Genus: Telopea

Telopea is a very small endemic genus with five species all occurring in Australia's south-eastern States. Stunning Waratah flowers set the bush "alight" in spring, standing out like flame torches. They are regarded as one of Australia's most spectacular and memorable native flowers. Waratah plants have evolved with hardy features such as rootstock for regeneration after bushfires and tough leaves coated with a raincoat-like veneer of cutin, to protect against moisture loss.

FUNDING FROM FLOWERS

Every year, a White Waratah Auction is held on 26 September: Waratah Day. Thousands of dollars are raised to support Australia's paralympic athletes.

During the 1960s an extremely rare, single bush of white flowering Waratah (*Telopea speciosissima*) was discovered in the New South Wales southern highlands, in a Sydney water-catchment forest.

TASMANIAN WARATAH

Eye-catching red Tasmanian Waratah (*Telopea truncata*) is endemic to Tasmania, with a widespread distribution in wet mountainous forests such as Cradle Mountain and Mt Field National Parks. Tasmania also has a rare bright yellow form of Waratah, (*Telopea truncata* var. *lutea*, left).

FLORAL EMBLEM

The high rainfall of the Hawkesbury sandstone area of New South Wales helps create an ideal habitat for New South Wales' floral emblem, the Waratah, (*Telopea speciosissima*). It's found from sea-level up to 1000 m. At least ten national parks in the Sydney Basin take pride in their naturally occurring Waratahs.

Above: Gippsland Waratah is a mountain-loving, frost-tolerant species It may reach 12 m. It's found in damp cool forests such as Bombala district in Vic and the far south coast of NSW.

the FACTS!

TWO AUSTRALIAN TOWNS are named Waratah, postcode 2298 in New South Wales and postcode 7321 in Tasmania

THERE IS ALSO A TOWN in New South Wales called Telopea, postcode 2117. Every spring for over 50 years the town of Telopea and Parramatta City Council have celebrated a Waratah Festival.

PLANTATIONS OF WARATAHS for the cut flower trade are grown in Australia, New Zealand, Israel, Hawaii, California, South Africa and Zimbabwe. Flowers are prized for their majestic blooms that last up to seventeen days.

IN THE LANGUAGE of flowers, Waratah is symbolic for long life.

WINGED WARATAH seeds take about three weeks to come up with a germination rate of about 80%. This is a high success rate for Australian native plants.

Water Plants
— taking it easy

Above and Right: Waterlilies float their leaves at the surface catching every available ray of sunshine.

Below: Freshwater fish and other aquatic animals depend on water plants for shelter, food and oxygen.

Water plants give life to freshwater ponds, billabongs, claypans, lakes and streams, pumping oxygen into the water and acting as cleansers helping to keep the water healthy and free from pollution. Aquatic plants also provide food and shelter for many living creatures. Nesting habitats amongst water plants are provided for birds such as pelicans and many other waterbirds. The Australasian Grebe (Tachybaptus novaehollandiae), depends on a fresh water habitat, building a nest constructed from aquatic plants.

the FACTS!

SOME AQUATIC PLANTS float but are tethered by their roots anchored in the mud.

AQUATIC PLANTS called submergents are underwater plants with flexible stems that carry out the process of photosynthesis. These provide hiding places and shelter for fish and other aquatic creatures.

A POND is classified as a body of water shallow enough for sunlight to reach plants at the bottom.

REEDS GROWING in water have rapid growth, as they need to reach the light as quickly as possible.

NARDOO

There are 65 species of Nardoo worldwide and six of these occur in Australia.

Nardoo (*Marsilea drummondii*) has been a staple food for Australia's Aborigines for thousands of years in Qld, NSW, Vic, SA, WA and the Northern Territory. Nardoo processing mills are permanently set up with sets of worn, flat grinding stones around the shores of lakes, billabongs, claypans and floodplains where the growth of Nardoo is prolific. Following heavy rain, Nardoo, an aquatic perennial fern, springs to life from underground rhizomes, forming a floating mat of green "four-leaf

clover" leaves. As the inland water evaporates during the dry season, the Nardoo dries up too, turning brown and leaving a bountiful crop of pea sized sporocarps (spore capsules) for Aboriginal people to harvest.

FLOATERS

"Floaters" are plants that float and can move with the water. Leaves and stems contain air pockets to enable them to remain on the surface of the water. The breathing stomata are on top of the leaves, taking in oxygen which is transferred down the stems to the roots of the plant. Their roots dangle down beneath the surface, are not attached to the bottom and take in nutrients from the water. Azolla (left) is an aquatic fern with an algal partner.

Conservation Watch

Two of the main concerns for water plants are pollution and changing water levels. Several species of overseas waterlilies and weeds have invaded, congested and blocked some of the waterways and waterholes in Australia. The dense matted cover that they form blocks out important light for other underwater plants.

Above: Giant Water Lily.

WATERLILIES

Waterlillies of the genus *Nymphaea*, have sweetly scented white, pink or blue flowers, mainly during the dry season in billabongs and lakes in the Northern Territory, Queensland and New South Wales. The Bininj and Mungguy people of Kakadu snack on raw waterlily stems that taste like celery. Rhizomes are baked — as are the nutty seeds, rich in oil and carbohydrates, to grind up and make damper.

Above: Jacanas depend on a waterlily habitat making a floating nest on a lily pad.

LOTUS

During a short three-day flowering, Sacred Lotus (*Nelumbo nucifera*) must complete a unique pollination process. When petals open, a delicate perfume entices beetles to visit, forage and transfer pollen. They are often trapped for the night as the petals close over them. The flower has the amazing ability to generate heat and maintain a temperature of between 30–35 °C, irrespective of the temperature of the day or night.

Right: Sacred Lotus (*Nelumbo nucifera*).

the FACTS!

LOTUS LILIES and other waterlilies are descendants of one of the very first flowering families to evolve.

THE SACRED LOTUS is India's national flower. In India milky sap from the stems is used as a medicine to cure diarrhoea. Aboriginal people in Australia have the same medicinal use for the sap.

IN CHINA almost all parts of the Lotus plant are eaten. Rhizomes, stems and the "pepperpot" female reproductive organ in the centre of the lily are all sliced up providing tasty crispness to stir-fry dishes.

LOTUS LEAVES can be used as umbrellas, sun hats and water carriers.

DURING EXTREME DROUGHT, swollen waterlily rhizomes survive underground, buried in dry mud, until waterholes are once again filled.

LOTUS SEED is known to retain the ability to germinate hundreds of years later.

COMMERCIAL CULTIVATION of Sacred Lotus (*Nelumbo nucifera*) in Australia shows great potential for the harvest of rhizomes as a food source, both for export to Asian countries such as Japan and for use in Australia.

INVENTIVE NATURE

Professor Wilhelm Barthlott, a German scientist, was curious about the incredible water-repellent nature of Lotus leaves and their amazing ability to remain totally clean. He investigated the waxy covering of the leaves and his discoveries led to his invention of a self-cleaning paint for the exterior of buildings.

Wattles
— sharing the land with gums

Above: *Acacia* is one of the two "signature" genera of the Australian continent. The trees are widespread and characterise many landscapes.

Family: Mimosaceae
Genus: Acacia

Acacias are said to have evolved on Gondwana up to 45 million years ago or more. This great southern land was made up of Australia, Antarctica, Africa, America, India and New Zealand. The world's acacias still grow in all these places, except New Zealand and Antarctica. It's estimated that there are between 1200–1350 species worldwide. Acacia *is Australia's largest genus of flowering plants, with 954 species. All through the year in different parts of Australia the land lights up in a flood of yellow as a multitude of widely distributed* Acacia *species flower.*

the FACTS!

WATTLE is reputed to cause hayfever. It is now thought that it is not the pollen, but strong scent, that causes an allergic reaction.

WATTLES are survivors. They search for underground water by sending their roots many metres into the ground. Fossilised acacia roots have been found 30 m down.

BEING LEGUMES, acacias have root nodules that fix atmospheric nitrogen, adding nutrients to the soil.

WATTLE SEEDS are so tough that they can wait in the ground and still germinate after twenty years or more.

RASPBERRY JAM (*Acacia acuminata*) timber smells just like raspberry jam.

IN THE LANGUAGE of flowers, the acacia flower is a solar symbol of rebirth and immortality.

WATTLE BLOSSOMS

Wattle blossoms are either pompom or lamb's tail shaped, in every shade of yellow imaginable. Two exceptions are a cultivar developed from a Victorian plant, Cinnamon Wattle (*Acacia leprosa*) called "Scarlet Blaze" which has almost red flowers and Queensland's very rare *Acacia purpureapetala* with purple flowers. Each bloom is made up of many individual flowers and the fluffy look comes from the stamens on every tiny flower.

Above: *Acacia lasiocalyx* has lamb's tail shaped wattle blossoms.

Right, top to bottom: There are many interesting variations on the theme of phyllode.

LEAF LOOK-A-LIKES

Most Australian *Acacia* species have made a very sensible adaption to cope with life in an arid land. To conserve water, many do not have true leaves, but leaf look-a-likes called phyllodes, which are tough, flattened or needle-like extensions of the stem. An exception is Cootamundra Wattle (*Acacia baileyana*), with true fern-like leaves.

LIVING HONEY POTS

Honey ants (*Melophorus bagoti*) excavate and build their underground nests as close as possible to stands of Mulga (*Acacia aneura*).

Worker ants collect honey-dew from lerp on Mulga trees and deposit it into the abdomens of storage ants which act as "living honey pots", never moving from the roof of their underground prison. In central Australia, Aboriginal women dig to find Honey Ants which make a delicious snack especially enjoyed by children. After the honey has been eaten the ant's head is thrown away.

WITCHETTY BUSH

Aboriginal women in Central Australia use digging sticks with sharp points to dig around the roots of Witchetty Bush (*Acacia kempeana*), as they search for witchetty — "witjuti" is a word from the Anangu language — grubs, which are the larvae of the Grey Moth (*Xyleutes biarpiti*). Roots with swellings show where Maku, (the Anangu people's name for witchetty grubs), can be found. They are collected in a coolamon, eaten raw or lightly roasted in hot ashes, and make great baby food.

Above: Honey Ants *(Melophorus bagoti)* make delicious snacks for Aboriginal children.

Left: An Aboriginal woman knows the local ecology and can find healthy food.

the FACTS!

GANG GANG COCKATOOS and Black Cockatoos rip bark from acacia trunks to find grubs to eat.

WAXEYES, New Holland Honeyeaters and Silvereyes drink the nectar from the tiny glands on the phyllodes of *Acacia* species.

SQUIRREL GLIDERS and Sugar Gliders need to live in forest with a wattle tree understorey where they can eat insects and the wattle sap.

SOME *ACACIA* SPECIES are host plants for several butterflies such as Imperial Hairstreak and Stencilled Hairstreak.

WATTLE TREES that produce lots of pollen, a rich source of protein for bee food, are Cootamundra Wattle (*Acacia baileyana*), Silver Wattle (*Acacia dealbata*) and Bodalla Silver Wattle (*Acacia silvestris*).

THRIPS have found a safe place to exist in Australia's harsh climate. Hiding under the bark of *Acacia* species, making little tent homes by joining phyllodes together, or irritating the plant into producing ball or cylinder-shaped hollow galls on the phyllodes, where they can live.

FLORAL EMBLEM

Golden Wattle (*Acacia pycnantha*) flowers in spring across Victoria and South Australia with one of the largest and most sensational ball-shaped blooms of all the Wattles. It is Australia's national floral emblem and has naturalised in parts of New South Wales and the east coast of Tasmania. Oil is extracted from the flowers for use in the perfume industry. Golden Wattle is also valued for its high tannin content.

Acacia pycnantha has a widespread distribution in southern Europe where it was introduced over a hundred years ago. It has been named as a weed by the World Wildlife Fund in their list, "Jumping the Garden Fence".

Above: Pink everlasting daisies flower for a few weeks under this small inland *Acacia* species.

the FACTS!

ACACIA SPECIES CONTAIN GUM that is a water-soluble polysaccharide known as Gum Arabic. Most Gum Arabic is produced from plantations of *Acacia senegal* in north-east Africa.

AUSTRALIA IMPORTS $1.5 million worth of Gum Arabic per year to use as a food thickener and for other uses too, like the adhesive on the backs of stamps.

ABORIGINAL PEOPLE COLLECT the sweet gum from Mulga (*Acacia aneura*). When mixed with water it dissolves and turns to jelly, which makes for a nice treat.

DURING AUTUMN, Vic's Western District Aboriginal people used to cut notches in Late Black Wattle (*Acacia mearnsii*) to collect the gum.

GUM was also collected from Silver Wattle (*Acacia dealbata*), Golden Wattle (*Acacia pycnantha*) and other *Acacia* species to eat and mix with water.

A STAPLE FOOD

For tens of thousands of years the people of Australia have understood the nutritional value of wattle seed. Freshly picked young green pods were lightly roasted and the seeds were eaten. Coast-dwelling groups in Tasmania and South Australia closely guarded their seasonal supplies of seedpods from Coast Wattle (*Acacia sophorae*). Sometimes there were even fights over this delicious food.

Fifty-six arid-region *Acacia* species are now known to have edible parts. Many are found to have approximately 20% protein, 8% unsaturated fats and 50% carbohydrates.

Researchers at CSIRO suggest that the addition of 10% wattle seed flour to processed flour would help increase the nutritional value of food.

WATTLE SEED INDUSTRY

Wattle seed has become an important taste sensation in Australia's booming bush food industry. Wattle seeds are roasted and ground into powder, not unlike coffee granules. It's mainly used as flavouring in bread, muffins, biscuits, cakes, pasta, ice-cream and also a coffee substitute.

The challenge has been to find *Acacia* species with seeds with a great taste that are suitable for human consumption. Trees need to be prolific, regular producers, to be easy to harvest and to have large enough seeds with husks that come off cleanly during processing. Commercial harvesting of wattle seed from Gundabluey (*Acacia victoriae*) occurs in the Flinders Ranges. *Acacia victoriae*, named after Victoria River in Queensland, is one of the main *Acacia* species used for the wattle seed industry.

FAMINE FOOD FOR AFRICA

In West Africa many people experience "hungry seasons" when food is in short supply and when malnutrition and disease affect large communities. One of these semi-arid zones is the Sahel, and plantations of Australian *Acacia colei* grown there are especially important for their edible seeds. Villagers at Maradi, in Niger, make a paste from *Acacia* species seeds.

Conservation Watch

Some of the wattles that are known to be Extinct in Australia are *Acacia kingiana* and *Acacia prismifolia.* Three more species are Critically Endangered and 28 are Endangered.

WATTLES WORLDWIDE

It's estimated that about two million hectares of Australian species of *Acacia* are grown in over 70 countries of the world, to provide economic, environmental and social benefits. Acacias are valued in Australia and overseas to help solve dry-land salinity, to fight soil degradation and for reforestation. Timber is used for firewood, furniture, building, tool handles and pulp.

MIMOSA

For well over two hundred years, Australia's Silver Wattle (*Acacia dealbata*), has been grown as "Mimosa" in southern Europe, and used for cut flowers and extraction of oil for perfume. Wattle perfume is so expensive that Australia mainly uses synthetic wattle oil at present. Mimosa Bush (*Acacia farnesiana*), has been cultivated in southern France since the 17th century, for the perfume industry at Grasse, where it is valued for the violet-scented oil produced by the heavily perfumed flowers. *Acacia farnesiana* is found growing in tropical areas of south-west USA and Mexico, Africa, Asia and Australia. It has a widespread distribution in northern Australia, from the east to the west, and in Western Australia it grows beside creeks north from Shark Bay. Aborigines used the sharp prickles to remove splinters and valued the wood for music sticks and axe handles.

Right: Despite its beauty and uses, *A. farnesiana* shrubs form thorn thickets and restrict access to watercourses.

the FACTS!

THE ROUNDED END of an acacia twig is perfect for Aboriginal artists to paint many small dots on their paintings.

STRING FOR FISHING was made by Gippsland people in Victoria, from the inner bark of Blackwood (*Acacia melanoxylon*). Yarra people called this tree "Burn-na-look" and found it to be useful wood for spear throwers and shields. Bark soaked in hot water soothed painful rheumatic joints.

DAME MARY GILMORE, author of *Old Days Old Ways*, who lived in Goulburn, NSW, in the 1870s wrote, "the wattlebark the Aborigines had taught us to make into a tan lotion for unbroken burns and scalds".

WARLPIRI PEOPLE of central Australia "smoked" a baby over smouldering leaves of *Acacia adsurgens* or *Acacia ancistrocarpa* to help cure diarrhoea.

WARTS WERE withered by piercing them with the prickles of Dead Finish (*Acacia tetragonophylla*).

JELLY BEANS, desserts, sauces and ice-cream often contain Gum Arabic. In frozen foods it prevents ice crystals forming.

Australia's
floral emblems

Most nations of the world select a special flower, tree or fern as a floral emblem. South Africa has — the Protea, *Japan — the Cherry Blossom, England — the Rose and New Zealand — the Silver Fern. The shape of the chosen plant must be identifiable enough to be stylised as a symbol for use on flags and coats of arms, on transport and on the clothing of national sporting teams.*

GOING FOR GOLD

Australia's national floral emblem is the Golden Wattle (*Acacia pycnantha*), which the national colours of green and gold were borrowed. This small tree was well selected, as it is a member of the largest genus of native plants in Australia — *Acacia spp.,* with almost 1000 species. The genus is a widespread one, and it is said that a species can be found flowering for every day of the year, therefore people in every State and Territory can appreciate wattles wherever they live. Acacia was first used as a national emblem in 1838, but it wasn't until 1 September 1910 that people in Sydney, Melbourne and Adelaide celebrated the first national "Wattle Day". Australia's official recognition of Golden Wattle took 200 years — in 1988, Parliament declared this species as Australia's national floral emblem. Wattle Day is now celebrated on 1 September each year. There was an interesting history of confusion (settled in 1992) about whether 1 August or 1 September should be Wattle Day. The confusion arose from differences in flowering times of regional wattle species. Sprigs of Golden Wattle give the Australian Coat of Arms a special glow.

NEW SOUTH WALES

Waratah (*Telopea speciosissima*).

Waratah is an Aboriginal word meaning "a tree with red flowers". Scottish-born naturalist Robert Brown (1773–1858) named this genus and species in 1810 after collecting specimens in the Blue Mountains and beside the Clyde and Hunter Rivers in New South Wales. Waratah has been New South Wales' floral emblem since 24 October 1962. People in New South Wales are so proud of their majestic red flower that they have named the State rugby team the Waratahs. Waratah Day is on 26 September.

VICTORIA

Pink Heath (*Epacris impressa*).

The pink variety of Common Heath (*Epacris impressa*) became the floral emblem in 1958 and the name Pink Heath is often used. The winter flowering of Pink Heath surprises people with its welcome addition of colour to bushland in southern Victoria. The plant is also found in New South Wales and Tasmania. A huge tapestry of Pink Heath, made by the Victorian Tapestry Workshop in 1980, hangs in the foyer of the Regent Hotel in Collins Street, Melbourne.

TASMANIA

Tasmanian Blue Gum (*Eucalyptus globulus*).

Tasmania is the only State that has a tree as its floral emblem. Aboriginal names include ballok (blue gum), wyeangta (large timber), eurabbie (blue gum). The Blue Gum was proclaimed Tasmania's floral emblem on 5 December 1962. It is Australia's most important eucalypt "ambassador" with economic importance in countries ranging from Algeria to India and Portugal. However, in California this tree has invaded areas of natural vegetation and been declared as an exotic pest plant of greatest concern.

AUSTRALIAN CAPITAL TERRITORY

Royal Bluebell (*Wahlenbergia gloriosa*).

This deep blue flower of high mountain forests and woodlands of ACT became the official floral emblem on 26 May 1982. It's such a lovely flower that some people cultivate it in their gardens.

NORTHERN TERRITORY

Sturt's Desert Rose (*Gossypium sturtianum*).

This hibiscus-like mauve flower with a crimson centre became the official floral emblem in 1974. Its name honours Captain Charles Sturt. The Northern Territory gained self-government on 1 July 1978, and that day they began flying the newly designed Northern Territory flag featuring a stylised Sturt's Desert Rose.

QUEENSLAND

Cooktown Orchid (*Dendrobium phalaenopsis*).

This attractive mauve-pink (occasionally white) native orchid became the State's official floral emblem on 19 November 1959 when Queensland had centenary celebrations. Its generic name comes from the Greek words dendron (tree) and bios (life), as these plants are found growing on tree trunks and branches. This epiphytic orchid lives in far north-east Queensland where heavy summer rains drench paperbark woodlands and vine thickets.

WESTERN AUSTRALIA

Mangles Kangaroo Paw (*Anigozanthus manglesii*).

This deep metallic-green and striking red paw-shaped flower became Western Australia's floral emblem in 1960. The importance of this plant to the export flower trade makes it an ambassador for Australia. The curved "kangaroo paw" shape arises from the plant's need to deposit pollen on the heads of birds which come to eat nectar. The birds then visit other flowers and pollinate them. The species name honours Captain James Mangle, an English collector of plants.

SOUTH AUSTRALIA

Sturt's Desert Pea (*Swainsona formosa*).

Meekyluka is an Aboriginal word meaning "flowers of the blood". Sturt's Desert Pea became South Australia's floral emblem on 21 November 1961. The common name honours explorer Captain Charles Sturt, who collected several of these flowers near Coopers Creek in 1845.

Bush Foods
— tucker & cuisine

CATHY HOPE

People are intrigued by the unique flavours of Australian bush foods, and gradually new taste sensations are appearing on menus across Australia as more culinary discoveries are made. Australia's four largest commercial plantations of endemic plants in order of size are Macadamia Nuts, Quandongs, Bush Tomatoes and Muntries. Ethnobotanists specialise in the study of the traditional knowledge and customs of any Indigenous peoples in their relationship to plants. Many Australian plants are edible. The traditional diet of Western Desert Aboriginal people is 80% plant-based and makes use of 140 plant species.

M. FAGG/ANBG

the FACTS!

NATIVE CURRANT (*Acrotriche depressa*, above) grows in mallee scrub in SA, WA, and Vic. Fruit is collected on Kangaroo Island for commercial production of a delicious jam.

PEPPERBERRIES, native to the cold high country of NSW, Vic and Tas, come from the plant Mountain Pepper (*Tasmannia lanceolata*), and are dried to be used as peppercorns for seasoning.

COMMERCIAL PLANTATIONS of Lemon Myrtle (*Backhousia citriodora*) are grown for oil extraction. Leaves are cool dried for powdered food flavouring which has its own unique lemony taste.

OLD MAN SALTBUSH (*Atriplex nummularia*) leaves are dried and flaked for seasoning.

AUSTRALIA HAS ONE Wild Orange (*Capparis mitchellii*), a green egg-shaped fruit, flavoured like both pawpaw and mango.

SIX NATIVE LIMES are found in Australia — five of them from rainforests. Lime marmalade and drinks are made by people who gather the tiny fruit of Wild Lime (*Eremocitrus glauca*), which grows in outback Qld, western NSW and part of the Flinders Ranges, SA.

A HARD NUT TO CRACK

Four species of macadamia trees are endemic to rainforests in Queensland and New South Wales. *Macadamia tetraphylla* is now a rare and endangered tree within its natural geographic range of less than 100 km.

Macadamia nuts (right), as well as being scrumptious, are a healthy food rich in iron, calcium, potassium, magnesium and six vitamins. These cholesterol-free nuts contain 78% mono-unsaturated oil and are claimed to have the highest oil content of any of the world's nuts. Macadamia nuts are so hard to crack but nature intended them to be tough to stop hungry rats and other animals and beetles eating them. Over the last few years, 25% of Australia's annual crop has been sent to China for the nuts to be cracked by hand — then the kernels are sent back to Australia.

Ergon Energy at Gympie in Queensland has established the world's first macadamia power plant, converting 5000 tonnes per year of waste shells from nuts into enough power for 1200 homes.

More than 800 Australian growers produce 40% of the world's macadamias. Ranked second and third are Hawaii then Central America.

DESERT QUANDONGS — "WILD PEACHES"

Quandong (*Santalum acuminatum*) of arid Australia is a small desert tree of the sandalwood genus that grows as a semi-parasite, taking nutrients from other plants' roots. The shiny red fruit look like cherry tomatoes but taste like tart rhubarb and peach. With a vitamin C content much higher than that of an orange, these fruit have always been most important for desert-dwelling Aborigines. Nowadays though, feral camels are eating so many fruit. Aboriginal people eat quandongs fresh, when fully ripe, and pound dried flesh into powder for cake making. Commercial plantations provide fruit for domestic and international markets.

Right: Desert Quandong's species name *Acuminatum* comes from its pointed leaves.

Conservation Watch

Collecting food from the wild is strictly regulated in Australia. Commercial manufacturers need to apply for a permit if they wish to collect bush food from the wild.

Above, left to right: Fruit of Deciduous Fig (*Ficus superba*); The fruit of this rainforest tree, Lilly Pilly (*Acmena smithii*) is used to make jams and sauces.

OUTBACK PRIDE PROJECT

Since 2000, the Outback Pride Project, developed by Gayle and Mike Quarmby of Reedy Creek, SA, is working with twenty Aboriginal communities, including Anangu, Pitjantjatjara and Yankunytjatjara peoples, to propagate, grow and sell their native food plants on a commercial scale. With the help of drip feeders to irrigate plantations, the fruiting season of bush tomato or desert raisin (*Solanum centrale*), called "Kutjera" in Kampurarpa–Pitjantjatjara languages, has been extended to eight months instead of the two month wild season.

Outback Pride also assists each community with revegetation plantings of traditional bush plants for food foraging, and children are encouraged to snack on the ripe fruits. Many children are eating up to half a kilogram of health-packed Kutjera per week, they are known to contain the highest levels of anti-oxidants in the plant world and also to contain high levels of potassium and vitamin C.

FIGS

The world has about 1000 species of figs. Most of Australia's 42 species occur in rainforests. A unique feature of figs is that the flowers are inside the fruit.

In central Australian arid areas, Native Fig (*Ficus platypoda*; "ili" in Anangu language) is the second-most important dryland fruit and provides fig feasts for Anangu people in the area. It flourishes at rocky places such as Uluru, where huge, spreading fig trees grow from rock crevices where seed has been dropped by animals.

SUN-DRIED TOMATOES

Tomatoes, capsicum, eggplant and potatoes all belong to the Solanaceae family.

Many *Solanum* species in arid Australia are quite poisonous, but fortunately there are six edible bush tomatoes that provide sufficient annual pickings for Aboriginal people who eat the small yellow-green fruit fresh, and also sun-dry any surplus tomatoes.

Bush Tomato (*Solanum chippendalei*) has edible pale-green, golf-ball-sized tomatoes that taste a little like rockmelon. Fruit of Desert Raisin (*Solanum centrale*) from Central Australia is collected by Aborigines from the bushes after the sun has dried the fruit.

the FACTS!

THE PEANUT TREE (*Sterculia quadrifida, below*), native to Australian and Papua New Guinean rainforests, has edible black seeds that taste just like peanuts.

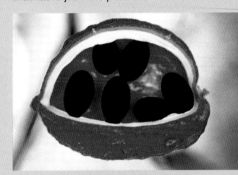

BUSH CUCUMBER (*Cucumis melo*), the only true melon native to Australia, belongs to the same family as rockmelon and cucumber. It is cultivated for commercial use by the Nepabunna Community in the Flinders Ranges, SA.

KAKADU PLUM (*Terminalia ferdinandiana*), the size and shape of an olive, has the highest vitamin C content of any fruit globally.

Below: Fruit of Desert Raisin (*Solanum centrale*) is just one of Australia's bush foods enjoyed by Aborigines.

Conservation
of Australia's flora

GREG HARM/SPP

OUR FLORA'S FUTURE

Australia has incredible biological wealth and this is recognised internationally. Education is a key factor in our flora's future. We need to promote a wider understanding of the biodiversity and sustainable use of Australian plants in relation to all living creatures. Days such as World Forestry Day (21 March), World Environment Day (5 June), World Habitat Day (5 October) and National Tree Planting Day (held in the last week of July) all help bring attention to the plight of plants. Strict quarantine laws monitoring the entry of plant material and plant-related products into Australia assist biosecurity. Several seedbanks in Australia act as custodians with their collections of seeds and are important conservation tools for maintenance of the diversity of flora. Local councils also strictly monitor and give advice about the type of vegetation to be planted in the locality and permits are required by private landowners to clear vegetation. Living collections of Australian flora in our Botanic Gardens are vitally important. National Parks and reserves have a vital role to play in conserving native plants by protecting and monitoring remnant vegetation and educating the public in this cause.

GREENING AUSTRALIA 2020 VISION

Greening Australia is a national project aiming to increase commercial tree crops, especially eucalypts, to three million hectares by 2020. Results of this work will include:

- less native tree felling from remnant vegetation;
- carbon sequestration;
- soil, air and water quality improvements;
- protection of biodiversity;
- conservation, business and employment opportunities; and
- throughout this process, land owners will be encouraged to retain native vegetation on their properties.

SOCIETY FOR GROWING AUSTRALIAN PLANTS

Society for Growing Australian Plants (SGAP) is a national society with membership groups all over Australia. One of the most important activities of this society is that members study, photograph, make records of and grow indigenous plants of their own locality. They are valued educators, passing on their passionate interest and knowledge of Australian plants through publications, wildflower shows and in local communities. They have "working bees" to re–establish vegetation in areas of concern.

RARE OR THREATENED AUSTRALIAN PLANTS

Western Australia has more than 45% of Australia's Rare or Threatened plants.

On 16 July 2000, the Commonwealth Government established the *Environment Protection and Biodiversity Conservation Act* and began keeping a national list of rare and threatened plants.

In 1979, researchers established a very comprehensive record of national flora which we consider to be of present and future concern. The Rare or Threatened Australian Plants (ROTAP) list has named 1100 species under threat.

Each State of Australia keeps records of its plants.

---

the FACTS!

SINCE 1770, 76 plant species are known to have become Extinct in Australia — but it is likely that up to 100 may have disappeared. Over 300 more species are seriously at risk of becoming Extinct.

SHRINKING AND ISOLATED populations of plants can lead to "in-breeding" which causes a declining seed production and loss of genetic diversity.

THE ACTIONS OF HUMANS in landscape clearing for agriculture, mining, forestry, road-making and urban and industrial development have caused loss of habitat for many plant species.

WILD HARVEST for the cut flower trade has reduced from 50% to 15% during the last 30 years, which is encouraging. Most native flowers are now cultivated for this $30 million export business.

EROSION, SALINITY PROBLEMS, weed invasion, competition and disease from introduced flora, herbicides and insect attack, have all added to a great environmental tragedy in this country.

INTRODUCED FERAL ANIMALS (such as the rabbit) and grazing by cattle and sheep have all added to the destruction of some plants.

LOSS OF SOME insect and bird pollinators has caused the reduction in population and range, or even the Extinction of some plant species.

GLOBAL WARMING is now the most serious threat to plant communities in Australia and is likely to speed up the loss of plant species.

PUBLICATIONS:

Attenborough, David. *The Private Life of Plants*. BBC London, 1995

Beattie, A. *Australia's Biodiversity*. Macquarie University & Reed, 1995

Blombery, A. *What Wildflower is That?* Paul Hamlyn, 1973

Boden, A. *Floral Emblems of Australia*. Australian National Botanic Gardens, Canberra, 1985

Breedon, S. & Wright, B. *Kakadu, Australia*. Steve Parish Publishing, 1995

Breidahl, H. Diminutive Drifters — Microscopic Aquatic Life. Macmillan Education, 2001

Brennan, K. *Wildflowers of Kakadu*. Jabiru, NT, 1986.

Brooker M. & Kleinig, D. *Field Guide To Eucalypts Vol 1*. Inkata, Sydney, 1983

Chippendale, G M. & Johnston R D. *Eucalypts Vol 2*. Nelson, Australia, 1983

Costermans, L. *Native Trees and Shrubs of South-eastern Australia*. Reed New Holland, 2002

Craig, G. *Native Plants of Ravensthorpe Region*. Ravensthorpe Wildflower Show WA, 1995

Dow, L. *Incredible Plants*. Allen and Unwin, Australia, 1997

Erickson, R., George, A., Marchant, N. & Morcombe, M. *Flowers and Plants of Western Australia*. Reed, 1973

Fuhrer, B. (Revised Edition) *Field Companion to Australian Fungi*. Bloomings Books, Melbourne, 2001

Gott, B. & Conran, J. *Victorian Koorie Plants*. Aboriginal Keeping Place, Hamilton, Victoria, 1991

Greenaway, T. *The Plant Kingdom*. Wayland, 1999

Greig, D. *Field Guide to Australian Wildflowers*. New Holland, 1999

Grey, P & E. *Fungi Down Under*. Fungi Map, Royal Botanic Gardens, Melbourne, 2005

Holliday, I. & Overton, B& D. *Kangaroo Island's Native Plants*. SA, 1994

Holliday, I. *A Field Guide to Melaleucas*. Hamlyn, 1989

Hope, C. *Wild Guide to Australian Native Plants*. Steve Parish Publishing, 2008

Jarman, S. & Fuhrer, B. *Mosses and liverworts of rainforest in Tasmania and south-eastern Australia*. CSIRO, 1995

Jones, D. & B. *Field Guide to Native Orchids of Southern Australia*. Bloomings Books, 2000

Kerr, G. & McDermott, H. *The Huon Pine Story*. Mainsail Books, Portland Victoria, 1999

Latz, P. *Bushfires and Bushtucker*. A D Press, Alice Springs, 1995

Low, T. *Bush Tucker*. Angus and Robertson, 1989

Low, T. *Bush Medicine*. Collins Angus Robertson, 1990

Mitchell, M. *Native Grasses*. Land Links, CSIRO, 2002

Simmon, M. *Acacias of Australia, Vol 1*, Nelson. Melbourne, 1987

Smith, K & I. *Grow Your own Bushfoods*. New Holland, Australia, 1999

Symon, D. & Jusaitis, M. *Sturt Pea*. Botanic Gardens and State Herbarium, SA, 2007

Urban, A. *Wildflowers and Plants of Central Australia*. Portside Editions, 1993

White, M. *The Greening of Gondwana*. Kangaroo Press, 1998

Wrigley, J. & Fagg, M. *Australian Native Plants*. Reed New Holland, 1998

Zola, N. & Gott, B. *Koorie Plants, Koorie People*. Koorie Heritage Trust, Melbourne, 1992

NATIVE GARDENS:

Queensland:
Anderson Park, Townsville — Pandanus collection.
Atherton Arboretum.
Brisbane Botanic Gardens, Mt Coot-tha Road, Toowong — Cycads, Palms.
Sherwood Arboretum, Jolimont Street, Sherwood, Brisbane — Kauri Pines.
Townsville Palmetum, University Road, Douglas, Townsville.
Cooktown Botanic Gardens.

New South Wales:
Mount Annan Botanic Gardens Mount Annan Drive, Mount Annan.
Royal Botanic Garden, Mrs Macquaries Road, Sydney.
Hunter Region Botanic Gardens, Pacific Highway, Motto Farm — Grevilleas.
Illawarra Grevillea Park, Princes Highway, Bulli.

Australian Capital Territory:
Albury Botanic Garden, 700 Smollet Street, Albury — 33 rainforest species of 10-90 years of age.

Australian National Botanic Garden, Clunies Ross Street, Acton, Canberra — 51,000 plants with about 7000 species.
Booderee Botanic Gardens, Village Road, Jervis Bay — coastal plants of SE Australia and Aboriginal interpretation of traditional plant use.

Victoria:
Royal Botanic Gardens, Birdwood Avenue, Melbourne.
The Australian Garden, Royal Botanic Gardens, Cranbourne.
Native Resource Garden (part of the Sandringham Heath Walk), cnr of Royal Avenue and Bluff Road, Sandringham.
Burnley Botanic Gardens (University of Melbourne), 500 Yarra Boulevard, Burnley.
Denbly Gardens, 9390 Princes Hwy, Killarney, — over 120 *Correa* varieties and cultivars.
Karwarra Australian Plant Garden, Lilydale — Boronia Collection.
Maranoa Gardens, Parring Road, Balwyn.
Peter Francis Points Arboretum, Coleraine (also Eucalyptus Discovery Centre, Old Shire Offices, Coleraine) — largest Collection of Eucalypts in the Southern Hemisphere.

Tasmania:
Royal Tasmanian Botanical Gardens, Queens Domain, Hobart — Epacrids.

South Australia:
Adelaide Botanic Garden, North Terrace, Adelaide.
Australian Arid Lands Botanic Garden, Stuart Highway, Port Augusta West — Australia's largest *Eremophila* Garden and annual *Eremophila* Festival.
Currency Creek Arboretum, 15 Rousillion Promenade, Old Reynella — Eucalypts.
Waite Aboretum, University of Adelaide, Glen Osmond — Eucalypts.
Wittunga Botanic Garden, Shepherd's Hill Road, Blackwood — Fleurieu Peninsula Flora.

Northern Territory:
Darwin Botanical Gardens, Gardens Road, Darwin — rainforest gully with hundreds of palm species and a mangrove boardwalk.
Alice Springs Desert Park, Larapinta Drive, Alice Springs.
Olive Pink Botanic Garden, Tuncks Road, Alice Springs.

Western Australia:
Kings Park and Botanic Garden, West Perth — W.A Flora.

Index